"I've never before seen a movie I've loved in quite this way...It's a pure emotional high, and you don't come down when the picture is over; you take it with you." —Pauline Kael, The New Yorker

"It's funny, it's rueful, it's satiric, it's saddening, and it's inescapably American...There's never been a film quite like it." —Saturday Review

"...is the genuine article: a splendidly gifted film, vibrant and immediate, with moments of true greatness." —Time

"...is comic, tragic, entertaining, jolting, spectacular and contemplative." —Cue

An Original Screenplay by
Joan Tewkesbury

BANTAM BOOKS
TORONTO · NEW YORK · LONDON

NASHVILLE
A Bantam Book/April 1976
All rights reserved.
Copyright © 1976 by American Broadcasting Companies, Inc.
This book may not be reproduced in whole or in part, by
mimeograph or any other means, without permission.
For information address: Bantam Books, Inc.

Published simultaneously in the United States and Canada

PRINTED IN THE UNITED STATES OF AMERICA

0 9 8 7 6 5 4 3 2 1

Perhaps the best thing about World War II was going to Sonja Henie movies, or the local train station to wave good-bye to the recruits as they went off to God knows where, smiling and clean in their new haircuts and uniforms. In 1946 the war ended, and shortly after that my best friend s mother had her picture on the front page of the morning paper. According to Hearst, she was a Communist and was going to be deported for her subversive activities. I worried, not about communism but about my friend; I thought she was too young to be without a mother. I read about Alger Hiss, Richard Nixon, a pumpkin, microfilm and Russians, Helen Keller, Sister Kenny, all of Pearl Buck's books and was taken to see Margot Fonteyn's first performance of SWAN LAKE on the Coast by Eugene Loring. Somewhere between President Eisenhower and my boyfriend's navy blue letter-man sweater, the Rosenbergs were executed, a lot of famous people lost their jobs because of the blacklists, and I couldn't see any of Charlie Chaplin's films because he was subversive, too.

OPERATION ABOLITION was screened, however, showing us college students what happened to uncooperative behavior. As the lights went on, someone handed out literature with "John Birch Society" written on it. A teacher raised the point that the film hadn't expressed the other point of view. "That was a consideration," said one of the literature hander-outers, "but not when one was devoted to the ideas of keeping America safe." A few blocks away, the Bolshoi Ballet gave a premiere performance of STONE FLOWER.

When the Democratic convention convened in Los Angeles, John Kennedy ran for President of the United States and everyone went down to the Biltmore Hotel to watch the action. It was very exciting and he certainly seemed to be having a good time with those crowds at Santa Monica beach and swimming with Marilyn Monroe. Against everyone else, he was Technicolor. When he won, we all cut our hair and tried to look like Jacqueline.

A few weeks before one of my children was born, Kennedy was shot, his shooter was shot, soon after that thirteen nurses were shot, then other people bought guns so they could shoot anyone that might try to shoot them, and the SPCA tried to shoot a deer that wandered into my backyard by mistake

Bobby Kennedy ran for the Democratic presidential nomination and everybody felt reassured. Not too many people asked Opal's offscreen question of Lady Pearl, "What about Cuba?" So he proceeded, drew out well, and was shot and killed just like everyone had been afraid he might be. The next day I went to London and was asked a lot of questions about the goings-on in the United States. What was I to answer; it was too complicated, none of us knew enough. I wasn't interested in politics even though it had been affecting me all of my life. I had a fling at freedom instead and began to comprehend my need to change something hard to define.

A few years later my friend, the one with the subversive mother, and I went to see a film where people moved at random, as people do, talked at the same time, like people do, and made cinema history when one of the actors walked into the football line and said to his opponent, "Okay bub, I'm gonna knock your fuckin' head right off." The audience went crazy. Suddenly there was the permission to say what one felt. The ramifications were endless.

Joan Didion wrote an essay about opposing issues that rub against each other forcing sensibility to waver, pulling first to one opposition and then to the other. Other people wrote things. Timothy Leary said things, Rudolph Nureyev defected to the United Kingdom and I began to teach at the university.

There was a new climate on campus. Angela Davis came and spoke. Abbie Hoffman came and was rude. William Kunstler just was. Exposure. Agnew attacked the universities for being elitist, Nixon proposed his Cambodian gamble, and students everywhere went on the rampage. At Kent State, the National Guard shot and killed four students and wounded eleven. An odd event, like they had been shot for malfunction of communication, as in please pass the sugar and you get the salt. Classes were closed. Our university was officially in mourning, arm-banded in black for Kent and red for Nixon's Cambodian decision. Outside observers crowded onto the campus looking for action, handing out invitations of pornographic intention, secretly hoping for an "incident," and declaring their disappointment when the students settled the issue with a sizable list of alternatives.

In the interim of reconstruction, I became aware of opposing issues happening simultaneously and the more my observership expanded, the more the duplicities were revealed. RASHOMON existed not because someone was right or wrong, but because we exist individually and simultaneously on different routes. Sometime that year Charlie Chaplin was reinstated in the annals of American film culture and given an Academy Award.

The day after Nixon was elected for the second time, the campaign where Wallace was shot, I was with Robert Altman and his wife in New York. There had been a storm of extreme proportions the previous night and as we walked down the street through the debris, Altman shook his head and said something about nature's omens. The election had been a lie.

As Watergate began to be an issue there was a small picture story in the morning paper. A young widow with her head on her twenty-five-year-old husband's casket. A secret service agent, he had been killed when a helicopter carrying agents to guard the President had crashed in the Bahamas. That was the day Geraldine Chaplin called Altman from Spain, asked some interesting questions about the CIA, and said yes, she would come to Nashville.

There is no possible way to explain the WHY to the structure of NASHVILLE. So, like the student who was asked to write about his summer vacation, I have chosen to write about the cow instead. Each actor gave freely of his or her histories, routes, connections, or nonconnections and, stirred by Altman's extraordinary capacities in overview and technical skill, rounded out the RASHOMON of the United States.

The day I left Nashville, Vassar Clemmens, violin case in hand, entered the airplane I was on. He had appeared briefly in the film with unencumbered authenticity. As I watched him I wondered if anyone would recognize him, or he me, or if anyone would wonder what was in his violin case. None of those things happened and when we got to Dallas, he disappeared like the young widow in the morning paper, the students at Kent, Joan Didion's essay, the Kennedys, Nixon, Eisenhower, Margot Fonteyn's SWAN LAKE, my friend's mother and all those soldiers on the train — out of sight but deeply ingrained in mind.

As you read the screenplay, remember this was written for a visual medium capable of giving assorted information to our perception on so many levels and in so many layers that we can't systematically record it. With that in mind, all you need to do is add yourself as the twenty-fifth character and know that whatever you think about the film is right, even if you think the film is wrong.

J. T. AUGUST 1975

As a spinning record jacket zooms forward and stops, showing us twenty-four cartoon faces packed on its confines, one of those hyper, record-salesman voices begins his diatribe.

MAN

Now — after years in the making. . .

The names of the songs run down on the right side of the screen as the cast names roll up the other.

MAN

Robert Altman brings you the long awaited "NASHVILLE" — with twenty-four, count 'em — twenty-four of your very favorite stars.

The music comes in, loud, seguing from one song to the next, and he continues with a hype on each until everything has whirled and spun and played through your senses.

MAN

And along with the magnificent stars — the magic of stereo sound and living-color picture — right before your very eyes, without commercial interruption.

Now the album with all the photos disappears backward into a block printed "NASHVILLE" which becomes the only thing on the screen for a moment as we hear:

VOICE, P.A.

Fellow taxpayers and stockholders in America. On the first Tuesday in November we have to make some vital decisions about our management.

EXTERIOR, STREET, DAY.

Pulling back from "NASHVILLE," we see the sign-covered garage door of the Tennesse State Headquarters of Hal Phillip Walker. The door rises and the Walker truck, the source of the speech, drives out onto the Nashville street.

VOICE, P.A.

Let me go directly to the point. I'm for doing some replacing. I've discussed the Replacement Party with people all over this country, and I'm often confronted with the statement "I don't want to get mixed up in politics." Or "I'm tired of politics," or "I'm not interested." Let me point out two things.

The truck now stops for a signal at the intersection of old music row as music starts to filter into the background.

VOICE, P.A.

Number one — all of us are deeply involved with politics whether we know it or not or like it or not. And number two — we **can** do something about it. When

you pay more for an automobile than it cost Columbus to make his first voyage to America, that's politics.
The signal changes and the truck continues down the road as
we follow the music track to the inside of a recording studio.
Cut.

INTERIOR, RECORDING STUDIO, DAY.

We pan past the glass booth containing spectators, engineers,
Haven Hamilton's son Bud, who looks like a cross between
Haven and Glen Campbell, Haven's mistress, Lady Pearl,
dressed in lilac, as usual, of some fifteen-odd years, and his
producer, Bob. Panning on around we hear Haven singing
"Two Hundred Years" and see some of Nashville's well known
back-up musicians and singers. Finally we see Haven himself
dressed in white, as usual, peering out from beneath his ill-
matched toupee. He is one of the kings of country music,
drinks milk, and tries to maintain a gentle attitude toward
everyone, although his temper often wins out. He has suf-
fered his share of losses and has learned how to handle all
sides of an issue at once. He takes his work very seriously. His
wife started traveling abroad after their other son was killed in
a senseless shooting accident, so they are a marriage of
name only. Bud has practically been raised by Pearl and was
too young to even remember his brother. Haven sings on
about why we've lasted two hundred years. We look back in
the glass booth and see a young woman loaded down with
camera and recording equipment, not to mention her own
patchwork ensemble topped off by a small hat with a musical
rhinestone pin, wander up to the glass and look at Haven as
though he were an exotic fish. Pearl, knowing Haven's idio-
syncracies, tries to get the girl's attention, but too late. Haven
has seen her and as she sits down, he stops the session and the
dialogue and confusion begin, everything running in overlap.

HAVEN
Hold it, hold it, everybody.

BOB
Hold it, everybody.

HAVEN
Bob.

BOB
Yes, sir.

HAVEN
Bob, I want to talk to Buddy. Buddy!

BUDDY

Ye-yes, sir, Dad.

HAVEN

Buddy — who is that woman in there with the hat on? Is she a friend of yours?

BUDDY

I don't know, Dad. She's. . .

And Opal interrupts but it doesn't matter because Haven just talks on.

OPAL

Hello, Mr. Hamilton. . .

HAVEN

Bob. . .

OPAL

I'm Opal, I'm from the BBC and I'm doing a documentary on Nashville.

HAVEN

Bob, Buddy, both of you — you know I don't allow no people visitin' when I'm recording.

OPAL

Did he hear me?

LADY PEARL

Yes, he heard you, dear.

HAVEN

I want no recording equipment in that studio. Buddy, go on escort the lady out.

BUDDY

Yes, sir.

HAVEN

If she wants a copy of this record, she can buy it when it's released. Would you please ask her to leave.

LADY PEARL

I'm sorry, there's no strangers allowed at all.

HAVEN

She's breakin' my concentration.

Opal stands.

OPAL

Mr. Hamilton, I'll be waiting outside for you.

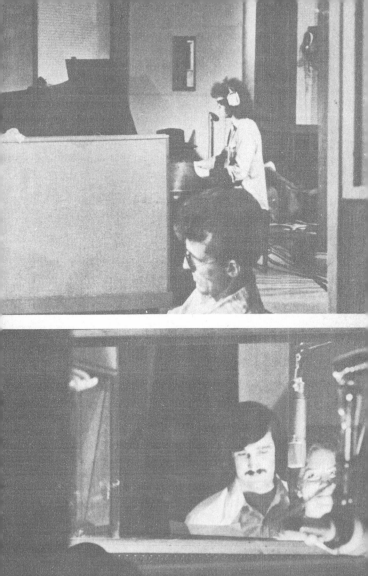

LADY PEARL
That's good.

OPAL
We'll have a little interview.
Finally, she leaves, smiling (Opal almost always smiles), with Bud who takes her into another studio in the building as Haven says—

HAVEN
All right, Bob; I want to do another one. Jimmy, you count off. I want to hear a little more Haven in this one.
Cut. 1

INTERIOR, STUDIO B, DAY.
In the background we hear hand-clapping and gospel singing as Bud opens the door for Opal to Studio B. It's smaller than A, so they stagger past the engineers and take a seat on the couch, Opal commenting as she goes.

BUDDY
This is Studio B right here. And, uh, I think they're doing some gospel...

OPAL
Oh, how sweeeet!

BUDDY

. . . recording of some sort. Hey Glenn, how are ya?

MAN

Hey, Buddy.

OPAL

It's lovely.

BUDDY

You don't mind if we sit in, just a little bit, do you?

MAN

Come on in.

BUDDY

Okay. Careful. . .

OPAL

It's so little. You know, I've been to all the important studios in London. They're all so enormous and very sort of impersonal.

BUDDY

We'll have to sort of keep it down a little bit so they can see, uh. . . hear what's going on.

OPAL

It's like a . . .

BUDDY

This is a black choir from, uh, part of it from Fisk
University here in town.

We see the all black choir dressed in turquoise robes with gold
satin trim, who sing "Do You Believe in Jesus" and answer their
one question with "Yes, I do" over and over again. There is one
female singer and she is white, Linnea Reese, somewhere in
her mid-thirties.

OPAL

Good Lord, lord love a duck!

BUD

The lady singing is a . . .

OPAL

A missionary.

BUD

No, she's not, she's a gospel singer. She's the wife of
our attorney.

Opal gives us a little of her ambiguous history.

OPAL

I was making a documentary in Kenya, and there was
this marvelous woman who was a missionary, that's
why I thought she was a missionary. She was sensa-
tional. She was converting Kukuyos by the dozens and
she was trying to convert the Masais, of course they
were hopeless, I mean (she laughs a slight laugh)
they have their own sort of religion, don't they.

She listens for "Jesus Knows What's in Your Soul" and continues:

OPAL

That really is fantastic. You know, it's funny you can tell
that. It's come down in the genes through ages and
ages and hundreds of years, but it's there. And take
off those robes and, and . . . and you're in darkest
Africa. I can just see their naked, frenzied bodies
dancing . . . dancing . . . Do they carry on like that in
church?

BUDDY

Depends on which church you go to.

And they look back at Linnea who bobs up and down, lost
somewhere in the rhythm of the song.

INTERIOR, STUDIO A, DAY.
We watch Haven and the back-up as they sing "I've lived through two depressions/and seven dust bowl droughts," when Haven pulls off his head set and shouts:

                    HAVEN
          Hold it, hold it.
The rest of them taper off as he shouts again.

                    HAVEN
          Hold it, everybody. Dammit, Bob. What's the name
          of the piano player, Bob?
We hear Bob on the intercom.

                    BOB
          That's Frog.
We see a young, hair-heavy pianist in current torn-Levi fashion, sitting and looking at the piano as if it made the mistake.

                    HAVEN
          That's Frog. He plays like a frog.
Haven puts the headset back on and, assuming a smile, says:

                    HAVEN
          We'll try it again. Jimmy—you count off.
INTERIOR, STUDIO B, DAY.
The group of gospel singers are rocking out in rhythm and at one point Linnea breaks up and completely disappears. The group continues as the last two credits come down.
INTERIOR, STUDIO A, DAY.
Back in Studio A, Haven reaches for the final crescendo and Frog misses again. Haven takes off the head set and slams it down on the podium.

                    HAVEN
          Dammit to hell.
We hear Bob on the intercom.

                    BOB
          Hold it, everybody.

                    HAVEN
          Bob—

                    BOB
          Yes, sir.

                    HAVEN
          What did you say the piano player's name was?

BOB

Frog.

HAVEN

Yeah, When I ask for Pig, I want Pig. Now you get me Pig and then we'll be ready to record this here tune.

BOB

Yes, sir.

Haven steps out of the booth, displaying his cactus-in-rhine-stone-covered outfit, and walks past Frog on his way out the door.

HAVEN

You get your hair cut; you don't belong in Nashville.

And we cut to:

EXTERIOR, AIRFIELD, DAY.

With "One I Love You" blaring in Franklin High School band time, we see the "Welcome to Nashville" sign on the airport tower. On the ground we see a three-ring circus of people inside the airport, airport security, people trying to get through the doors and out onto the steaming pavement, TV cameras, reporters, Chamber of Commerce, the high school band, and at least fifty twirling majorettes from the Tennessee Twirling Institute. Hal Phillip Walker's signs can be seen through the glass, and all the airport traffic proceeds, occasionally drowning out the sound of the TV commentator and all the preparations for Barbara-Jean's arrival.

ANNOUNCER

This is Bill Jenkins on special assignment for Channel Two News here at Metro Airport. We are awaiting the arrival of Barbara-Jean, who, as you know, has been away for special treatment at the Baltimore Burn Center. Already, prior to her arrival, Barbara-Jean fans and other supporters are here at the airport. They are at the moment being held inside the terminal by security police. Other members of the Chamber of Commerce are on the way. Also, at this report, Haven Hamilton will make an appearance here at Metro Airport.

Cut.

INTERIOR, TERMINAL, DAY.

A lean paratrooper, Pvt. Glen Kelly, somewhere in his late twenties, and spit and polished to perfection, walks through the confusion at a record booth.

                    KELLY

Ma'am.

                    GIRL

Mmhmm?

                    KELLY

Excuse me, am I late for Barbara-Jean's plane?

                    GIRL

No, I don't think so, but they're not gonna let you out
there.

                    KELLY

Thank you, ma'am.

And he continues into the crowd packed against the glass,
some of them to see their idol, others just there because
there is a crowd and they're curious.

                                                        Cut.

EXTERIOR, AIRPORT, FRONT, DAY.

We see the Walker truck move behind a fellow on a black
and white, three-wheeled motorcycle. Walker's message
drones on as the praying mantis-looking vehicle stops in front
of a limousine being polished by Norman, a would be sing-
er-songwriter in a chauffeur's uniform. The Tricycle Man steps
out of his machine. He is long and thin, looking a little like a
praying mantis himself. As he walks into the terminal, he
takes off a green scarf and magically turns it red, and to
Norman's astonishment ties it back around his neck and goes
into the building. During all of this, Walker's truck, with its
incessant speaker system, spews out a message about the
government forcing its citizens to swallow a camel.

                                                        Cut.

EXTERIOR, AIRFIELD, DAY.

Barbara-Jean's blue and white Cessna touches down and
starts to taxi toward the anxiously waiting crowd, as the announcer continues his blow-by-blow account of her arrival.

                    ANNOUNCER

Her plane has touched down... it's down the taxi-
way now... and will be arriving at any moment now
onto the ramp area directly here, practically in front
of us here at Metro Airport.

                                                        Cut.

INTERIOR, AIRPORT RESTAURANT, DAY.

The Tricycle Man is seated at the end of the counter, rearranging
the salt for his salad, via the air, in a magic trick that Wade

KER .

nation

AL PHILIP
WALKER

REPLACEME   RTY

PRES   NT

Coolidge watches closely. Dishwashing is one of Wade's three jobs a day. He's black, spent twenty-seven years in jail, studied law in jail and got himself out with the aid of thirteen lawyers, about four months ago. An older man sits down at the counter, Mr. Green. He and his wife live in Nashville, had an antique and fix-it shop before he retired. Now they rent rooms in their house to would-be musicians and Bible salesman. A little deaf and very tired, he's come to pick up his niece, Martha, whom he last saw when she was about twelve or thirteen.

GREEN

Ahh . . . Miss . . . May I—

SUELEEN

Hi.

Sueleen Gay has red hair and is lost somewhere in 1940 and her fantasy about being a singer. One is struck by her wide-eyed innocence and overt sex display. She reminds you of those girls who came to Hollywood to become movie stars and went home older because of the trip.

GREEN

Hi . . . a . . . I'll have a caramel sundae.

SUELEEN

We ain't got no caramel sundae.

GREEN

Butterscotch?

This continues until they arrive at strawberry. Sueleen goes off and shouts her order to the air and Wade pulls her over, points to the motorcycle man, and they stand watching him do his trick. Wade can't believe it.

WADE

Sueleen, did you see what he just did? Took the thing off the salt and threw it in the air. Did you see that?

Sueleen walks over to the Tricycle Man who smiles behind his yellow glasses and truly looks like a magical bug.

SUELEEN

How'd you do that?

At the other end of the counter, the fellow next to Mr. Green crunches his crackers with his fist and talks to him. Mr. Green, not really wanting to talk but also not wanting to be impolite, tells him that his wife is sick as Sueleen brings the sundae.

MAN

I'm sorry to hear that.

GREEN

Oh, it's just one of those things.

MAN

Happens in the best of families.

GREEN (slight laugh)

Yea.

Sueleen has wandered back to the Tricycle Man, who doesn't speak but just watches her happily.

SUELEEN

I wrote me this real hot song. You want to hear it?

He nods.

It's called "I Never Get Enough."

He nods again.

All right.

She looks around and then begins to sing, not very on-key, and half does gestures to her song about a girl who "always wants more and more." On the other side of Green, Delbert Reese, Linnea's husband, sits having a cup of coffee. He can't believe his ears but he can't take his eyes off the translucent-skinned redhead. He's a lawyer for Haven Hamilton, Barbara-Jean and others. He and Linnea have been married about fourteen years, just before he started law school. He's younger than he looks and wears clothes that make him look wider than he is. He's engaging, is the caretaker of other people's problems and never asks much from anyone but to be liked. His home is his castle but he doesn't understand it somehow. He and Linnea have two children who are deaf. All of his activities have kept him too busy to learn the hand language, so Linnea acts as an interpreter. The voice of the loudspeaker announces the arrival of the plane he is waiting to meet. He rises, puts on his dark glasses, and overtips Sueleen who continues to sing "I Never Get Enough."

Cut.

INTERIOR, TERMINAL, DAY.

A group of girls run past Reese in red, white and blue outfits with Hal Phillip literature in their hands. The thinnest, leggiest girl you've ever seen stands like a stork on a pair of platform shoes made to look like feet. She has hennaed hair. Her short-shorts and tiny, strapless bra meet like an eraser at the top of a pencil. She checks out the greeters, but her uncle hasn't arrived yet. Mr. Green is in for a big surprise. An older man walks past Reese and he walks forward.

DEL
John Triplette?

The older man sees his waiting friend but the younger man
behind responds.

TRIPLETTE
You looking for me?

Del turns and is surprised by his youthfulness. They've never met
before. John is here to put talent together for a televised fund-
raising concert for Hal Phillip Walker, the independent presidential candidate whose headquarters we saw at the beginning of the film. Triplette graduated from UCLA somewhere in
the midfifties. He makes one remember white dinner jackets,
Balboa, California, Phi Delta Theta summer dances with paper
lanterns, and John F. Kennedy's dynamic smile. He is a lawyer,
and his wife has just divorced him because he was never at
home, he has no children. Del sticks out his hand and is
bumped by an extremely beautiful young woman who continues to walk toward the terminal. He looks after her for a
moment and then back to Triplette.

DEL
A . . . oh . . . John?

TRIPLETTE
Hello. What's your name?

Del comes forward and takes off his glasses.

DEL
Del Reese, I'm sorry. Forgive me these damn glasses.
Thanks for coming out.

They both smile and chuckle. Triplette says how much he likes
the girls in costumes, which Del repeats as they walk into the
terminal.

Cut.

EXTERIOR, AIRFIELD, DAY.

Outside, the majorettes trick and twirl as the bands play and
more people come toward Barbara-Jean's plane. Haven and
Bud and Lady Pearl round the corner in their white jeep. An
ambulance approaches, too, and the announcer announces
as Haven steps down into a cluster of gracious businessmen
dressed in Dacron summer suits.

Cut.

INTERIOR, TERMINAL, DAY.

Mr. Green has found his niece slightly taller than he is and

hardly what he expected. She leans over and tells him that she's changed her name from Martha to L. A. Joan, Mr. Green nods, not having heard at first, then hearing, then not sure that he's heard what he heard, so he continues.

GREEN

Aunt Esther wants to see you. She's in the hospital. She doesn't feel too well.

At this point a long lanky fellow with a beard, guitar, and a very friendly attitude toward the four stewardesses who are walking with him, wanders over to a cigarette machine in back of Mr. Green. L. A. Joan has spotted him.

L.A. JOAN

Wait a minute. I think this guy's a rock star.

GREEN (not hearing)

And she'd like to see you.

L.A. JOAN

Wait, hang on...

She leaves Green in the center of the floor as she pulls out an album and plops it down on top of the machine.

L.A. JOAN

Hi. Can I get your autograph? You're Tom, aren't you. Tom, Bill, and Mary?

Tom Frank is handsome in a wayward way, and his music-fan following is large and taken care of personally whenever he can tend to it. He looks at her before he signs the album.

TOM

Jesus, you oughta stop that diet before you ruin yourself.

INTERIOR, COUNTRY MUSIC STAND, DAY.

We see the beautiful young woman, Mary, and her guitar-toting husband, Bill. They are the other two-thirds of Tom, Bill, and Mary, and are in Nashville to cut an album. Their last one was a couple of years ago and had a standout single, "It Don't Worry Me." Until Tom got his plane ticket, they hadn't seen each other in a few months and thus far with great forethought has managed to lose them. Bill is extremely ambitious and seems to carry the responsibility of the other two like a stage mother. He pulls up to a picture of their album in front of the record stand and sees a large picture of Connie White with a Hal Phillip Walker sticker attached to her bosom.

BILL

Hey — they have our album here. (to the girl) How's it

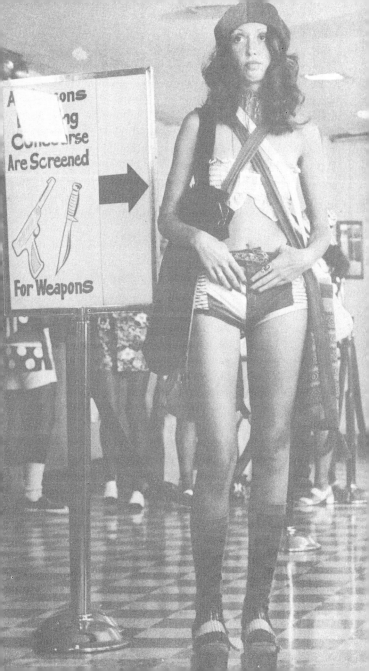

selling?

Mary pulls him along.

> I'm the handsome one in the front. I...I don't have
> my glasses on but...Wait a minute. Hal Phillip Walker
> looks exactly like Connie White.

EXTERIOR, AIRFIELD, DAY.

Delbert and Triplette make their way through the people
and doors. A few fans and girls get loose, but armed security
stuff them back inside. John tells Del he likes bands. Haven
signs autographs as Pearl continues to talk whether anyone
listens or not.

> ### LADY PEARL
> Little kids, honey—they practiced every day for a
> whole month...

> ### HAVEN
> Yes, they're so nice.

> ### LADY PEARL
> Isn't that cute?

Haven finishes his last autograph.

> ### HAVEN
> I think that'll cheer her up and, Pearl, shut up.

Pvt. Kelley, the paratrooper, stands at the window listening to
the announcer tell how Barbara-Jean was tragically burned in
an accident in a fire as a child, which brought she and Haven
together. He wrote his first hit tune for her. And as Del and
Triplette approach Barnett, the announcer continues how although she is recovered it requires skin grafts and regular visits to
the burn center. Del walks to Barnett, a rotund energetic man,
who is Barbara-Jean's husband and manager. Barnett has
made her his life. He was an orderly in the hospital where she
recovered as a child and stayed until she was fifteen when they
were married. She wrote songs, met Haven, who introduced
her to a public who's adored her ever since. Barnett runs
interference for her schedule that is usually too crowded, often
making himself appear foolish in his intensity. He has a thick Fu
Manchu mustache, a brown leather jacket, and a soiled
necktie. Contrary to the basic contention of Tom, Bill and Mary's
hit song, everything worries Barnett.

> ### DEL
> Hello, Barnett!

Barnett throws up his arms in dismay—

BARNETT

> I got no time right now, Jesus —

As Del scratches his head and Triplette, who's never quite seen anything like it, laughs and breaks the tension.

Cut.

INTERIOR, TERMINAL, DAY.

Tom stands near Pvt. Kelly and fends off a cute blonde's plea for him to vote for Walker. He tells her he never votes for anybody. Then, he looks at the paratrooper, whose been saving all his leave time so he could come to see Barbara-Jean at the new Opryland, and says:

TOM

> Hiya, sargeant — kill anybody this week?

Through the glass we see Haven introducing his son, Bud.

HAVEN

> Come on, Buddy, just say hello. My son Buddy. He just graduated from Harvard Law School. We're just trying to give him the breaks we never got. Buddy, say hello to the people.

EXTERIOR, AIRFIELD.

BUDDY

> Hi. . .

HAVEN

> Thank you, Buddy.

LADY PEARL

> Oh, that's lovely.

The twirlers complete their routine and the band breaks into Barbara-Jean's theme song as the announcer, Haven, and media people move forward to drink her in as she steps from the plane and starts walking to her waiting fans. Air traffic continues behind her. There is an intensity about her that is thrilling and terrifying all at the same time. She is small-boned, fragile-looking and beautiful in the sense of 1940's beautiful movie stars. She would rather cook for forty than most anything else except singing. She writes her own songs that are full of her philosophy. She is available to anyone who can get near to her with a problem, and one can see that Barnett has his hands full.

Cut.

INTERIOR, TERMINAL, DAY.

Bill and Mary watch her as Norman, late, comes up in back of them and taps their shoulders, saying "Hi, Bill" to Mary and

WELCOME TO
NASHVILLE

"Hi, Mary" to Bill. They moan their responses to the joke and
start outside as Wade tries to pry Sueleen from the window.

WADE
Are you gonna ride into town with me or not?

SUELEEN
You better go without me. I'm gonna wait 'cause I
think she's gonna sing.

WADE
Who, her? She ain't gonna sing. She don't sing unless
she gets paid. Now come on.

Cut.

EXTERIOR, AIRFIELD, DAY.
Outside, Barbara-Jean has just received a bouquet of flowers
from the smallest majorette, who just finished running
through a row of flags to get to Barbara-Jean.

BARBARA-JEAN
Oh, you little beauty. Thank you so much. Ah...
Now she looks up and addresses those adoring fans.
I'd like to thank you for coming out to meet me today.
It's great to be home. It's hot as a firecracker...
Everyone laughs.
Me and the boys are goin' to be at the Opry this week.
And like my granddaddy always used to say, "If
you're down by the river, I hope you'll drop in."
She waves and signals off as Lady Pearl says "Isn't that lovely."
Then Barbara-Jean looks at the people in the terminal pack-
ed behind the glass.
Barnett — who are all those people inside there?

BARNETT
It's just airport security, darlin,' because of all the
hijackers.

BARBARA-JEAN
Did they come to see me?

BARNETT
They can see you pretty good, darlin.'

BARBARA-JEAN (not having that)
Well, I'd like to go in and say hello.
Barnett sighs, looks at the crowd, and helps her off the
podium, followed by Haven and the rest of the news media.
With everyone talking at once, as usual, the commentator is
commenting on her every step. Just after Barnett tells her to

look out for the water, she turns and collapses. Everyone closes in screaming, people break the security guard inside the building and pour out in curious droves. Pvt. Kelly stands forlornly as three band members and the hospital attendant lift her to the stretcher.

Cut.

EXTERIOR, AIRPORT, DAY.

L.A. Joan and Mr. Green walk to their Nash, Triplette and Delbert to Del's Cadillac, Wade and Sueleen to Wade's on-the-repair pickup, and Tom to a sun-roofed Volkswagen filled with stewardesses. Walker's P.A. voice continues.

VOICE, P.A.

Who do you think is running Congress? Farmers. Engineers? Teachers? Businessmen? No, my friends, Congress is run by lawyers. A lawyer is trained for two things: to clarify and confuse.

In the background, Norman tries to find his keys and sort out the luggage. Bill takes over for a moment with the keys, but finally Mary steps in and finds the correct key as the voice continues.

VOICE, P.A.

Did you ever ask a lawyer the time of day? He told you how to make a watch, didn't he? Ever ask a lawyer how to get to Mr. Jones' house in the country? You got lost, didn't you. Congress is composed of five hundred and thirty-five individuals — two hundred and eighty-eight are lawyers.

Now all the cars and Wade's truck proceed to back out of their spaces, accompanied by some fast-picking music and the inescapable voice of the P.A. At the terminal parking gate, the camera pans down to the Tricycle Man, followed by Wade, followed by Tom, Mr. Green, then Delbert, then Norman chauffeuring Mary and Bill, and a bus with a picture of Connie White on the outside and Pvt. Kelly inside, which takes off the parking arm as it leaves the lot. The last car to leave is Hal Phillip Walker's van on which is written "New Roots for the Nation."

Cut.

EXTERIOR, AIRFIELD, DAY.

On the now deserted airfield, the TV announcer speaks quietly to the viewers as a girl with a Walker poster steps up behind him and smiles into the camera.

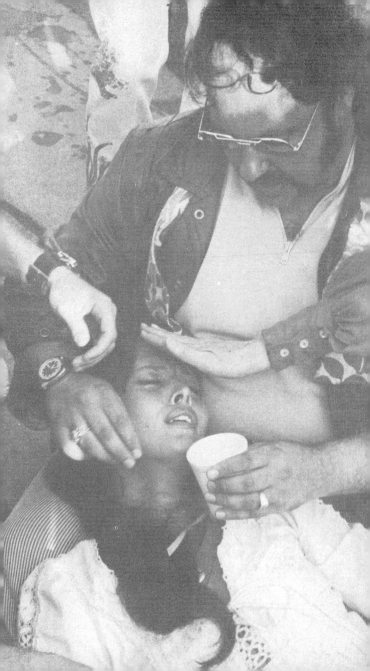

ANNOUNCER
She quietly collapsed here on the sidewalk in a sort of
a faint; that's all we've been able to determine from
Dr. Boulan at this moment.
A guard steps in and pulls the poster girl out of the frame.
That's it for the moment from Metro Airport for Chan-
nel Two News. This is Bill Jenkins reporting.

Cut.

EXTERIOR, FREEWAY, DAY.
The Walker truck moves on to the freeway.

VOICE, P.A.
Our national anthem. Nobody knows the words. Nobody can sing it, nobody understands it. They don't—

At this point a yellow couch has fallen from one of the fast-
moving vehicles, and as a car with a boat swerves to miss it,
the freeway becomes a mass of screeching, sliding and crash-
ing, creating an enormous jam destined to make one spend
an hour waiting, like it or not. Haven, in his jeep with Pearl and
Bud, slow to the pile-up, and ahead of them are Pvt. Kelly in
the bus, Wade's truck, Delbert and Triplette, Mary and Bill and
Norman, Mr. Green and L. A. Joan, and Tom and the stewardesses. The Walker P. A. is still in operation.

P.A.
Let's change our national anthem back to something
people could understand. Something that would
make a light shine in their faces.
People get out of their cars, first to see if they can help, and
then just to walk around. Tom signs autographs through the
roof of the car and further back in the traffic, behind a popsicle
truck, sits Linnea in her station wagon with Opal writhing in the
front seat.

OPAL
I feel sick.

LINNEA (rolling down the window)
Just a minute, just a minute. Hello—would you
please go to the popsicle truck and get us a couple
of sweet ices.
She hands some money to a passer-by, as Opal exaggerates
grotesquely.

OPAL
There must be about twenty cars; they're all piled up,
one on top of the other. Some are upside down. I saw

a leg sticking out... I wish my cameraman had been here. I need something like this for my documentary. It's America, all those cars smashing into each other and all those mangled bodies.

Barbara-Jean's ambulance, with sirens blaring, pulls up on the grass in order to bypass the jam and takes off toward town. An old green Chevrolet pulls out behind and attempts the same maneuver but it stalls. Delbert gets out of his car and walks over to it. Kenny Fraiser sits inside, looking innocent and burned out at the same time. He is basically a tourist-drifter who lives at home with his mother in Terre Haute, Indiana, when he's not on the road. He sits sweating in his broken car.

DEL
You think you can pull out there?

Kenny looks at him.

KENNY
You want to come in and try it?

Nearby, L.A. Joan, listening to a transistor radio, asks Mr. Green if there are any rock stations, and he talks about his wife, Esther.

GREEN
It's hard to really say. You see, after they opened her up, they decided they'd do an exploratory, you know? They ended up giving her an overhaul...

Bill bargains with a street vendor selling turtle footstools. As a dirty stream of water shoots up from Kenny's car, the P.A. says something about 12,000 major crimes committed.

He jumps back to avoid getting burned and after a moment slams the hood down on the mistake. Then he walks to his car whose back seat is loaded with Walker posters and literature. He pulls out a jacket that his father gave him a long time ago and a violin case with one of those have-your-picture-painted-for-a-dollar portraits of himself on it. He starts to walk back through the cars and up the hill to an overpass. Opal sits with her microphone interviewing Linnea.

OPAL
Uh... have you any children?

LINNEA
Yes. I have two children. I have a boy and a girl.

OPAL
Isn't that nice. How old are they?

LINNEA

Twelve and eleven.

OPAL

Do they want to be singers like their mommy?

LINNEA

Oh, well. . . my, my children are deaf. They're deaf, they were born deaf.

Opal is horrified.

OPAL

Oh, my God! How awful!

LINNEA

No, it's not.

OPAL

It's dreadful!

LINNEA

No, now wait just a minute. That's not so. I wish you could see my little boy. I want you to see my little boy.

OPAL

Oh no, I couldn't. I couldn't stand to see —

LINNEA (interrupting)

He has an incredible personality.

OPAL

The sadness of it all.

Inside a bright red pickup truck, a grisly looking farmer with a limp named Star sits beside his wife, Winifred, who looks like she has blonde feathers for hair. More than Sueleen Gay, she would like to be a famous singer and write songs. Star met her when she was twelve or thirteen outside a laundramat just after he got out of the Navy. They got married, she had babies, wrote songs, and runs away to Nashville every now and then to cut a demo record with $25 from the egg money. She calls herself Albequerque and believes in the liberation of women, while Star believes in getting by on what you've got. He hates, absolutely hates, country western music.

ALBEQUERQUE

. . . and ya see what happens, he made a million dollars on a flyswatter, because it had a red dot in the center.

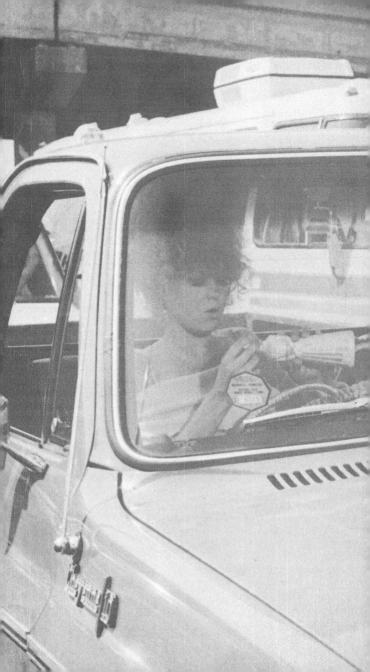

STAR

Flyswatter?

ALBEQUERQUE

Yes, sir, that's right. Red dot. He was sitting in the buffet and he was eatin' and he saw a woman an' she was swattin' flies and she, he said, well what makes the difference between y'know flyswatters? Because it was to do with the industrial revolution. . .

Nearby Triplette and Del discuss fans.

TRIPLETTE

See, the thing with these country people is they have a real grass roots appeal.

DEL

Oh hell, they got fans alright.

TRIPLETTE

And they're the people that elect the president and if you line up a lot of movie stars. . . I mean, I think people down here feel that movie stars are eccentric. Crazy. Communists.

DEL (laughing)

Well. . .

TRIPLETTE (laughing)

A lot of them are.

Albequerque makes out her list of things to do.

ALBEQUERQUE

An' then I want to go to the Grand Ole Opry to have. . .

STAR

God, oh, forget that—

ALBEQUERQUE

No! 'Cause I have to have my record signed. . .

STAR

Goddam it. I don't like that music.

He opens the door and gets out.

I'm going up front and see what the hell's going on.

ALBEQUERQUE (not giving up)

'Cause I've got this gold record and—

She holds up a yellow plastic single of a Connie White song, as Star, with his cane, makes his way through the stopped traffic, telling people to get away from his truck.

ALBEQUERQUE

Well, shit.

And stuffing her belongings into her basket, she opens the truck door and takes off in the direction of the hill and overpass, leaving Star behind. Opal meanwhile has made her way to a large tan bus that reads "Tommy Brown's Back in Town." She knocks on the door and asks a good-looking beige negro if she can speak with the owner of the bus. She has no idea what Tommy Brown looks like. We see Haven under a blue umbrella signing autographs and arguing with Pearl, who gets increasingly louder as she tries to make her point. She sings a line, Haven corrects her, Buddy is noncommital, and Pearl ends up making her point by saying the song was a hit. In the background we see Albequerque climb over the bridge railing and walk toward town.

INTERIOR, BUS, DAY.

Opal sits inside the bus with seven or eight black people. Other than Wade, they're the first blacks we've seen. Unbeknownst to Opal, Tommy Brown, the man who let her in, is putting her on.

OPAL

Will Mr. Brown be here soon?

BROWN

Oh, yeah. He's in the back there changing. He has to put his makeup on. Whenever he's having an interview, he likes to get all prettied up.

The people in the bus suppress their laughter.

OPAL

Well, he must be a marvelous person. I mean, to have all you lovely people working for him. I mean I know the problems in the South.

BROWN (smiling)

Oh — well — he's very, uh, liberal. By the way, I'd like you to meet his wife. This is Joy.

Opal turns to a delicate-looking mulatto and is shocked.

OPAL

Mrs. Brown?

JOY (assured)

Yes. . .

EXTERIOR, FREEWAY, DAY.

As the wreckers clear up the snarled traffic, the Tricycle Man, accompanied by music, hops on his machine and starts it up,

and with his hat brim flapped back against the wind rides off into town.

INTERIOR, BARBARA-JEAN'S HOSPITAL ROOM, DAY.

As the Walker truck passes Barbara-Jean's window, a bevy of busy people do their best to make her feel at home. The whole thing takes on a festive air, like a cocktail party, and well-wishers stream in and out. Bud hangs pictures and Barbara-Jean's cousin, Jewel, brings in flowers.

BARNETT

You've outdone yourself, Bud.

JEWEL

We got pictures just the right height. Look at this.

BARNETT

Oh yeah, little bird again.

BARBARA-JEAN

That's beautiful, Jewel. I remember when you gave that to me.

BARNETT

I remember I almost threw it out.

INTERIOR, HOSPITAL HALL, DAY.

Mr. Green plants L. A. Joan in the hall outside Barbara-Jean's room. He tells her to wait while Aunt Esther, across the hall, freshens up. A guard stands at Barbara-Jean's room refusing to let a photographer in. Delbert and Triplette walk in past the official. Pvt. Kelly looks in through the door.

INTERIOR, BARBARA-JEAN'S ROOM, DAY.

The noise level is reaching a new pitch.

DEL

How ya doing?

BARNETT

Del, I got no time...

DEL

I know, I know. I just stopped by.

Barnett hovers near Barbara-Jean anxiously.

BARNETT

I'm under the gun.

BARBARA-JEAN

Del, how ya doing?

They shake hands and she asks him sincerely,

How's lawyerin'?

DELBERT
Honey, fine, just fine. You get some rest now.
He sits down on the bed and Triplette leans back against the wall and watches the circus unfold. More flowers arrive.

JEWEL
These are from Connie White.

BARNETT
Put them up there with the other carnations.

BARBARA-JEAN
Del, can you crank me up a little?

DEL
Sure thing.

BARBARA-JEAN
Thanks.
Bud is pounding nails in the wall to hang pictures on and some white flowered "HH" (Haven Hamilton) horseshoes are brought in.

BARNETT
White carnations again? If I told him once I told him a hundred times, they're too funereal. Bud, Bud, what're you doing there! This is a hospital; this ain't no construction sight. Come on, no pictures, go out and build a dam, goddamit!
Befuddled, Bud leaves, passing Tommy Brown and his wife who enter with an orchid. Opal pulls up in the doorway and is not admitted, much to her verbal disgust.

BARBARA-JEAN
Look who's here — Mr. Brown.
Brown and Barnett shake one of those soul-brother hand-shakes that Barnett doesn't know all the words to, so it dissipates clumsily in the air.

BARBARA-JEAN
How do you do? So nice to see you. You look as beautiful as a big black butterfly I saw out on the highway near my house the other day.

BARNETT
My God, I'm getting jealous. You better get outa here.
A young woman with a white coat and clipboard squeezes through the crowd. She's Barbara-Jean's doctor.

DOCTOR
Barnett, I need to talk to you.

BARNETT
You got it. All right, everybody out, doctor's got to talk turkey.

Everyone starts their good-byes, and Delbert brings Triplette forward.

DEL
Barnett, there's somebody I just want you to meet.

BARNET
Who's that?

DEL
John Triplette from California.

BARNETT
Triple, nice to...

TRIPLETTE (sincerely)
Triplette, nice to meet you.

BARNETT (cutting him off)
Okay, doctor, come on and give us some good news so we can get outa here.

INTERIOR, HOSPITAL CORRIDOR, DAY.

As Delbert and Triplette leave, Opal stops them with her microphone.

OPAL
Are you a relative?

TRIPLETTE
No.

OPAL
Can you tell me how she is?

TRIPLETTE
She's fine. It's her husband I'm concerned about.

As they pass by Bud, L.A. Joan comes up to him, introduces herself and asks him for a light, which he gives her. Mr. Green comes out to get her but she sends him back, begging his pardon for having interrupted her. She continues her conversation with Bud and smoking her cigarette with her blue fingernails.

Cut.

EXTERIOR, HIGHWAY, DAY.

In long shot we see Albequerque, who, full-length, looks somewhat like a miniskirted Barbie doll, and Kenny walk toward us down the highway.

KENNY

What do you do?

ALBEQUERQUE

Well, I. . . I'm on my way to town to become a country music singer or star.

KENNY

Yeah?

ALBEQUERQUE

Yeah.

KENNY

What're you gonna do if you don't?

ALBEQUERQUE

If I don't? Oh, I can always go into sales.

KENNY

Like ladies clothes? Like what you wear?

ALBEQUERQUE

Oh, no. I know all about trucks. I'd go into trucking, I guess.

She keeps glancing over her shoulder.

KENNY (laughs)

You're kidding me.

ALBEQUERQUE

No, I'm not kidding you. I'm in a truck enough, and then I know how to fix motors and all that, so—

KENNY

Nobody buys trucks from a girl.

ALBEQUERQUE

No, I been fixing motors for a long. . . why do you say that because now what's happened is if I can't sell trucks, then I can't. . .

She looks behind her and sees Star's truck and starts to run out of frame.

ALBEQUERQUE

Don't say you saw me.

She is gone by the time Star pulls up, honking his horn before stopping.

STAR

Hey, you haven't seen my wife, have you? Sort of an ordinary-looking lady.

KENNY
No — you going into town?

STAR
You're not one of them country singers, are you?

KENNY
No. Can you give me a ride?

STAR
All right, get in.

KENNY (climbing in)
Thank you.
And as they drive off —

STAR
You look like a guy I was in the Navy with. Yeah, he wouldn't take a bath so we pee'd in his bed to get him discharged.

Cut.

INTERIOR, SUELEEN'S BEDROOM, DAY.
We see Sueleen standing, looking in her closet mirror. She is stuffing white sweat-socks padding into her push-up bra under a blue-front, zipped jump suit with big cutouts on the side. By looking, we know every cent goes into her career that will never get off the ground because it can't get out of that room. She smiles and practices her introduction into the mirror.

SUELEEN
Hi. My name's Sueleen Gay and I'm here to sing you all a couple of songs I wrote and I sure hope you're gonna enjoy it, honey — 'cause I know I'm just gonna enjoy singing 'em to you. The first one is called "Let Me Be the One."

She holds up one finger and smiles to her image in the mirror.

Cut.

INTERIOR, HOSPITAL, DAY.
L.A. Joan has donned some kind of India cotton wrapper that matches her fingernails, and she and Bud start toward the elevator as Mr. Green comes from Esther's room

BUD (politely)
What about your aunt and uncle?

L.A. JOAN
Oh, it's cool. I can see them anytime. What kinda car you got?

BUD (politely)

I have a little one.

Mr. Green calls, "Martha," but it's too late, she's gone down the elevator. He turns away, putting on his most cheerful face to hide his disappointment and walks back into his wife's room.

Cut.

EXTERIOR, PICKING PARLOR, NIGHT.

We see the Picking Parlor sign, some Walker girls, and hear bluegrass music.

Cut.

INTERIOR, PICKING PARLOR, NIGHT.

Inside, the camera pans across a huge picture of John Kennedy, to the four Misty Mountain Boys playing and singing "Mississippi River," and then to the patrons, including Haven and Tommy Brown at one table, and Bill and Mary at another. Mary looks over her shoulder as Bill asks her why she didn't wear an outfit to match his.

MARY

Cause I didn't want to wear it.

BILL

You're supposed to wear the blue dress when I wear the blue —

MARY (interrupting)

I don't want to dress like twins any more. We're not twins, we're a trio.

At this point, Kenny, looking wide-eyed, enters the door that Lady Pearl stands guarding.

LADY PEARL

Come in, young stud, and sit down.

She pulls out the empty chair at Bill and Mary's table and plops him down in it. Mary moves closer to Bill and through the applause for the end of the song, Kenny looks sheepish and apologizes.

KENNY

I'm sorry. . . sorry. . .

Bill shrugs.

BILL

That's okay.

Mary turns to Bill, saying softly in his ear —

MARY

He looks like Howdy Doody.

EXTERIOR, DEMON'S DEN, NIGHT.
L. A. Joan and Bud drive up in his white Volkswagen jeep to
the redwood nightclub with the devil's head on the corner.

BUD

This here is the Demon's Den.
INTERIOR, DEMON'S DEN, NIGHT.
Inside, one ever so small girl named Sheila and one ever so
tall girl named Patti introduce themselves as the Smokey
Mountain Laurel. In not the same color but matching dresses,
they sing ''Troubled Times'' in clear as bell voices. Star is seated
at the bar having a beer while Sueleen bobs up and down to
the music behind them. Tom sits at a table with a couple of
blondes as Opal, who is trying to snap off a few photos, finds
him in the lens and he looks at her oddly.

OPAL

Oh sorry, oh Tom!

TOM

Yeah?

OPAL

Tom, hello! I was looking for you. This chap told me

you were here.

TOM

Who are you?
She shakes his hand.

OPAL

I'm Opal from the BBC.

TOM	**OPAL**
Hello Opal from the BBC.	Good. Ladies, you don't mind if I sit. . . crowd you a little.

And she slides in, ousting the already-on-the-way blondes.

Cut.

INTERIOR, PARLOR, NIGHT.
We see Pearl onstage and a sea of checkered tablecloths and applauding people below.

LADY PEARL

All right. I've got a couple of announcements. We got some stars here tonight.
We see Bill and Mary look around.

BILL

Can't be us.

PEARL

Tommy Brown's back in town! (applause) Tommy Brown, stand up and show it all off.

Panning, we see Tommy stand and bow, a little embarrassed by the display. Haven sits smiling and clapping but Wade, who's had one beer too many at the bar, shouts:

WADE

Tommy Brown's the whitest nigger in town!

Immediately, Haven rises from his three glasses of milk and helps Tommy and the others outside.

HAVEN

It's getting late. I'm sorry. I'm so very sorry.

Kenny watches Wade as Brown and his wife and the people from the bus get up and start out the door.

HAVEN

This is not typical . . . now I hope—

WADE

He oughta drink some of that milk—it fits his personality! Hey—he's leaving. Shit, he's still the whitest nigger in town and I ain't gonna change my mind

about that... I tell you that right now—
Wade starts out after the Brown party and Kenny tries to stop
him. Wade throws him to the ground and all hell breaks loose.
Mary and Bill leave and Lady Pearl shouts above the other two
fights that have started as a result of Kenny falling.

LADY PEARL
All right, boys, cool it. I got two guns here.

Cut.

INTERIOR, DEMON'S DEN, NIGHT.
Patti and Sheila ask the man at the bar, whose name is Trout, if
they did okay and he nods yes. They walk off to a booth near
Opal, who is counting into her tape recorder in French, and
past L. A. Joan who enters the bathroom. Trout shouts: —

TROUT
Hey, Bear, how about a couple of beers for the
Smokey Mountain Laurel...
He then turns to Sueleen.

TROUT
Okay, honey. What's your name?

SUELEEN
Sueleen... Sueleen Gay.

TROUT
Sueleen Gay? You're on next.
She turns to her accompanist.

SUELEEN
Come on, Bunkie.
Someone in the background talks about Hal Phillip Walker smoking funny-looking cigarettes and he's an admitted "homo," as Sueleen grabs the mike and looks directly at the Tricycle Man who sits in a booth.

SUELEEN
Hi, y'all. My name's Sueleen Gay.
She repeats the introduction she did in front of the mirror and begins, with her gestures, to sing "Let Me Be the One." Oozing coy sex, she does. Sing, she does not. Or at least not on pitch. Star turns away, shaking his head no. Patti and Sheila can't believe their ears. Albequerque makes her way down the bar in back of Star. She stops to talk to Frog, the piano player from Haven's session. Sueleen continues in the background.

ALBEQUERQUE
I'm looking for Frog.

FROG

You got him.

ALBEQUERQUE

Oh. . . well. . .

FROG

You want a beer?

ALBEQUERQUE

No thanks, this is business. What I was wondering — I'm making a demonstration record.

FROG

At a recording studio?

ALBEQUERQUE

And. . . uh

Star turns, having recognized her voice, and shouts:

STAR

Winifred!

She responds without thinking.

ALBEQUERQUE

What? Oh, you!

She turns and runs. Star limps out after her as fast as he can —

                          STAR
            Goddamit! Come back here!
The phone rings behind the bar and Trout picks it up.

                          TROUT
            Demon's Den?

                    DEL (voice-over)
            Is Trout there?

                          TROUT
            Yeah, this is Trout.

                                                    Cut.
INTERIOR, REESE HOME, NIGHT.
In an entirely beige den, we see Delbert talking on phone.
Triplette looks at the pictures on the wall.

                          DEL
            Listen, we're gonna have a little fund-raiser.

                    TROUT (voice-over)
            Yeah—you need some talent?

                          DEL
            Yeah, talent... Uh, tell ya what. The fellow I'm work-
            ing with is here and I'm gonna put him on. John
            Triplette's his name. He's from California.

                    TROUT (voice-over)
            Put him on.
Del hands the phone to John.

                          DEL
            Uh, Trout—this fellow's name is Trout.

                JOHN (not believing the name)
            Trout?

                          DEL
            Yeah.

                          JOHN
            Hello, Trout?

                          TROUT
            Hey, John, how are you?

                          JOHN
            Ah, fine. Listen, as Del told you, we're putting a
            smoker together.

                          TROUT
            Right.

JOHN
Monday night. Anyway, we need a certain kind of young lady to entertain the troops.

The camera pans right with Del as he crosses into the dining room. Linnea is there with the children. Jimmy is telling in both sign and spoken language about his experience passing his swimming test, as his sister helps set the table. Linnea listens intently and Del tries, means well, but is unable to comprehend too much of what's going on. Jimmy is a special child and so is his sister. It is as if their being born with one handicap gave them special capacities in other areas.

DEL
I'm sorry I sprang this on ya, hon.' I just asked the man if he wanted to come home to dinner and he said yes. What were you, just out there on the freeway all by yourself?

She is still intent on the story.

LINNEA
Wasn't it hot! I thought I was gonna burn up.

DEL
Yeah, terrible. You learn anything at school today, Jim?

LINNEA
Hush, let him tell it.

DEL
Well . . .

Jimmy continues, as does Triplette in the other room.

Cut.

INTERIOR, DEMON'S DEN, NIGHT.
We hear Sueleen singing in the background.

TROUT (voice-over)
I have a saucy, saucy, redhead who is dynamite, absolutely dynamite.

JOHN
Saucy —

TROUT (voice-over)
Her name's Sueleen Gay.

JOHN
Well, listen, if she's half as provocative as her name, we're all home free.

Cut.

INTERIOR, DEMON'S DEN, NIGHT.
Trout moves to Sueleen, telling her that she was dynamite. Her looks have conquered all. L.A. Joan walks out of the bathroom with a blonde "natural" wig on and taps Bud on the shoulder. He looks at her, doesn't recognize who she is, and steps aside so she can pass. She gives him a look of disbelief, shrugs and walks over to the Tricycle Man who does a magic trick and produces a glass of water. Trout juices Sueleen for the swell job he got her over the phone.

> TROUT
> I mean, you knocked 'em out.

> SUELEEN (squeals)
> I did?

> TROUT
> Honey, listen — you're gonna be a star.

> SUELEEN
> How do I...?

> TROUT
> I got you a job while you were singing.

> SUELEEN
> You did?

Bud gives up waiting and he passes Opal and Tom as he goes out.

> TROUT
> A friend called, very heavy, and there's a party Monday night. Now the pay isn't much, a low-budget thing. About ten dollars.

> SUELEEN
> Oh hell, I don't care about the money.

> TROUT
> That's the attitude. You are. You're gonna be a star.

Tom excuses himself from Opal and goes to the phone.

Cut.

INTERIOR, REESE HOME, NIGHT.
Everyone is seated at the table having supper when the phone rings. Linnea excuses herself, gets up, and goes in to the kitchen.

INTERIOR, KITCHEN.
She picks up the phone as Delbert and Triplette talk about the values of campaigning in the next room.

LINNEA
Hello?

TOM (voice-over)
Hi, Linnea?

LINNEA
Hmm...

TOM (voice-over)
I'm here.

LINNEA
Who is this?

TOM (voice-over)
This is Tom.

LINNEA
Just a minute, just a minute; I have something in my mouth. (she swallows) I was eating dinner.

TOM (voice-over)
You haven't changed a bit, have you?

LINNEA
Now, who is it...?

TOM (voice-over)
This is Tom, don't you remember?

LINNEA
No, I don't believe I do.

TOM (voice-over, laughing)
We met in the control room at the recording studio two months ago.

LINNEA
Oh yes... How are you?

TOM (voice-over)
Yes, I'm fine. How are you?

LINNEA
I'm just fine. What're you doing in Nashville?

TOM (voice-over)
Recording for a couple of weeks. I'd really like to see you.

LINNEA
Well, why don't you come by the house. The children would like to meet you.

>   TOM (voice-over, with a slight laugh)
>   That's not exactly what I had in mind.
>   Look, I find you very attractive and I'd like to see you.

>   LINNEA
>   Well, I think it would be fine if we had dinner some
>   night here at the house. You've never met my hus-
>   band Del, have you?

>   TOM (voice-over)
>   I see. You can't talk now. Okay, listen. I'll call you later,
>   I'm going home and I'll call you when I get there.
> He hangs up. She continues talking to the dial tone.

>   LINNEA
>   Well, I'd like to...a...well, all right. I'll talk to you
>   later. Thanks for calling.
> She hangs up and we pan with her into the dining room as she
> sits back down. Delbert interrupts John to talk to Linnea.

>   DEL
>   Who was that, Babe?

>   LINNEA
>   Oh, down at the recording studio. Someone, uh...I
>   left a...some music down there.

Cut.

INTERIOR, HOSPITAL CORRIDOR.
Barbara-Jean's security guard stands talking with the nurses at
the desk about guns and the two or three times he's had to
use one, not to kill anyone, of course. Pvt. Kelly gets out of the
elevator with a bouquet of flowers he picked from the hospital flower bed. He makes his way down the hall to Barbara-
Jean's room.

Cut.

INTERIOR, BARBARA-JEAN'S ROOM.
Pvt. Kelly enters the darkened room which now looks like a
funeral parlor. Barbara-Jean looks like Sleeping Beauty. He
puts the flowers in her water pitcher, then sits down in the chair
beside the bed and writes the following note.
>   "When I die and go to heaven
>   I want you to come along
>   and be an angel with me."

Cut.

EXTERIOR, HOSPITAL, NIGHT.
It's after midnight and we see the Tricycle Man drive around
the hospital's circular drive and stop at Mr. Green's Nash.

Green sits waiting for her on the porch. L. A. Joan is in back of him and swings her legs over the Tricycle Man's head.

L.A. JOAN
See you later, alligator.

She waves good-bye as he leaves and walks to Green who stands and walks to her

L.A. JOAN
Am I too late?

GREEN
Well, Esther's asleep now. She's looking forward to seeing you, but we'll see her in the morning.

DAY TWO
EXTERIOR, INTERSECTION ROUTE 10 & 40, DAY

It is early morning and the Walker van is in the gas station being filled. The P.A. system is on. We see the Tricycle Man move along the highway and stop at an intersection. Panning around, we see a white, abandoned car parked in a lot. Continuing the pan, we see Star in his red truck, craning out the window as he drives, looking in all directions at once for Albequerque. As he passes the white car, the form asleep in the back under a Walker poster moves and gets up. It is Albequerque. She looks around for a moment and as Star heads back into town, she gets out of the car and makes her way across the street, intent only on getting to the gas station bathroom.

P.A.
If the chairman of the board or the president of your company had been running your business the way Washington has been running our business, you'd be asking a lot of questions. And you would find out what you already know. We have some problems that money alone won't solve. Now I know something about money. Anybody who grew up without it knows a lot about money. I know more about money than some of the rich because I never had any until I was twenty-seven. I know something of what money can do and more important, I know something of what it can't do. Does it make sense to let the petroleum industry

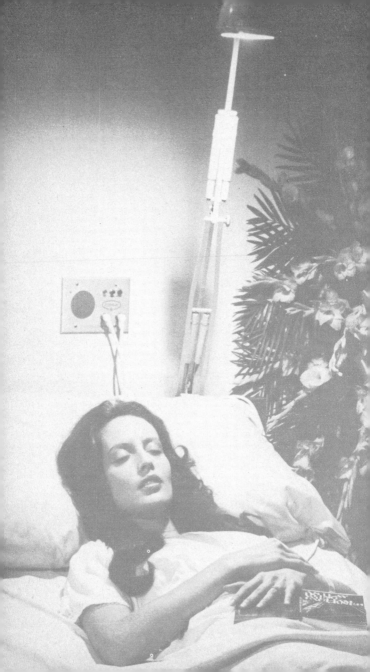

Two cars, in maneuvering to avoid her, collide, and their drivers start their day with a string of obscenities and a fistfight, while Albequerque, unaware of the chaos she has caused, makes it safely to the other side of the street.

EXTERIOR, STREET, DAY

Kenny walks along a residential street lined with ''Room for Rent'' signs. The Walker truck passes by with its ongoing dialogue as he looks for an address in the paper. He finds it and turns up the walk. Mr. Green is having a snooze on the front porch swing. Kenny hesitates for a minute and then knocks on one of the porch columns waking him up.

boost their prices at will? The little filling-station owner out there in his khakis—he can't charge a penny more. To tax the salary of people at poverty-level income, then turn around and give back in food stamps twice the amount of taxes...

Cut.

If there is any cleaning up to be done, we're going to have to do it. The Lord is not going to do the replacing and the powers that be are certainly not going to replace themselves. The old truth remains—there is no such thing as a free lunch; if the books are balanced, we're going to have to balance them.

KENNY

Hello—

GREEN

Oh, yes sir.

KENNY

You got a room for rent?

GREEN

Oh yeah, I'm Mr. Green. That's me, I'm Mr. Green.

KENNY

I'd like to see it.

GREEN (puzzled)

You'd like to see it?

KENNY

Yeah.

GREEN

What's your name again?

KENNY

Kenny, Kenny Fraiser.

GREEN

All right, Kenny, right this way.

He opens the screen door and they go inside.

INTERIOR, GREEN HOUSE, DAY.

It's Esther's house, really; dark wood walls, old-fashioned, sliding wood doors, flowered wallpaper—everything has a place and is in it. Kenny is shown the front bedroom and comments softly that it looks like his room at home. The picture on the wall even looks like Kenny. Green shows him the toilet down the hall, and tells him that his wife is in the hospital nearby. After asking him if he is a musician, Mr. Green introduces him to his niece, L. A. Joan, who is dressed in gold satin hotpants, top, and is trying on yet another wig. The headset she has on blares out a raunchy rock tune.

GREEN

She's from California.

Kenny nods to her. She shakes his hand in rhythm to the song and gives him a smile.

KENNY

Thirteen-fifty?

GREEN

That's right and you can have breakfast with me if you want. Of course, you'll have to help me with the dishes.

KENNY (smiling)

Fine. Let me put this down and I'll pay you.

INTERIOR, BARBARA-JEAN'S HOSPITAL ROOM, DAY.

Pvt. Kelly is asleep in the chair where we left him last night.

When the nurse comes in to awaken Barbara-Jean, she star-tles him and he leaves very quickly, saying he must have the wrong room. The nurse watches him leave as Barbara-Jean stirs.

> NURSE
>
> Time to get up, Barbara-Jean.

> BARBARA-JEAN (stretching)
>
> Good morning, Louise.

> NURSE
>
> How are you? Did you have a nice rest?

> BARBARA-JEAN
>
> Yeah, I was having a dream.

Cut.

INTERIOR, REESE HOME, DAY.

As Delbert stands in the kitchen about to hard-boil himself an egg, Linnea sits with the children in the den teaching them the hand gestures for "Sing, Sing a Song."

INTERIOR, HOTEL ROOM, DAY.

We see Opal's clothes in a heap on the floor. Tom's "It Don't Worry Me" plays on the tape recorder. The television set is turned on to the Saturday-morning Electric Company and Tom sits sullenly in bed smoking, next to Opal who is still asleep. He nudges her roughly.

> TOM
>
> Wake up.

She rolls over, looks at him, and then back over to her tape recorder, which has been running. She says something into it and turns it off.

> OPAL
>
> Oh, God. For a moment I thought I was in Israel. I don't know why. Certainly not the decor. I must have been dreaming.

Tom moves his lanky frame to the phone and searches for a number among an array of others. His song continues in the background as Opal, in toe-less red socks, moves across to her clothes next to a tray of dirty dishes.

> OPAL
>
> I spent about a year on the kibbutz... I was very romantic about that sort of socialism at the time.

She gathers her clothes and Tom dials the phone as his re-corded voice sings:

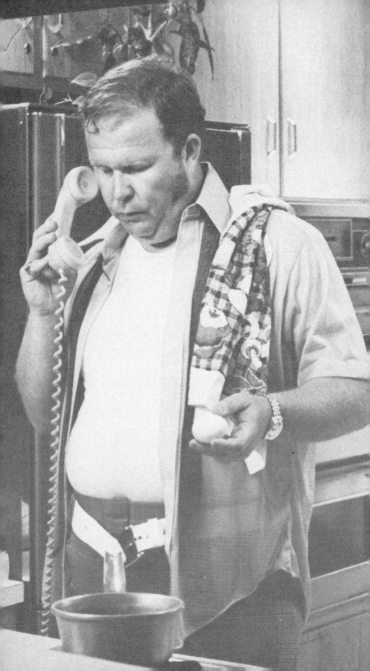

TOM (song)

Say this train don't give out rides
Well, it don't worry me.
All the world is taking sides,
But it don't worry me.
Economy's depressed, not me,
My spirit's high as it can be.
And you may say that I ain't free,
But it don't worry me.

Cut.

INTERIOR, REESE HOME, DAY.
The phone rings by Delbert in the kitchen.

DEL

Hello.

TOM (voice-over)

Hello, can I talk to Linnea please?

LINNEA (voice-over)

Uh, this... Del, I'm on the phone. This is Linnea.

DEL

Okay.
He does not hang up. He continues to listen and watch the
water he's boiling.

TOM (voice-over)

How are you? Listen, I'm sorry I didn't call sooner but I
got tied up.

LINNEA (voice-over)

Who is this?

TOM (voice-over)

This is Tom.

LINNEA (voice-over)

Tom who?

TOM

Oh, come on.

LINNEA (voice-over)

Look, I don't know who you are & I don't know why
you're callin' me but I want you to stop!

TOM (voice-over)

Oh, come on, honey. You know you want to see me.

LINNEA (voice-over)

I never said any such a thing and I don't want you ever

calling here again and I'm not fooling with you! I mean it and don't you ever call here again. Good-bye.

We hear the click on Linnea's phone and Del hangs up on Tom's "Linnea... hello?" Del steps back to the stove, picks up an egg, drops it into the water and burns his fingers. The mystery hangs in the air for a moment and then he calls to his wife.

DEL

Who was that, babe?

Linnea still sits with the children at the table in the den.

LINNEA

Just some crazy person been calling here, and the next time he calls I want you to get on the phone and tell him you're gonna get the police on him.

Del looks at his egg and replies as though nothing has happened.

DEL

Okay.

As Linnea and the children go back to singing "A Simple Song."

Cut.

INTERIOR, HOSPITAL CORRIDOR, DAY.

Pvt. Kelly stands at the hospital desk writing a postcard to his mother to tell her that Barbara-Jean is recovering. Mr. Green and L.A. Joan get off the elevator with a bunch of home-grown daisies. L.A. Joan looks like something out of *Paris Vogue*. As Mr. Green and the nurses exchange amenities, she peruses the desk, sees Kelly, smiles and walks over to him with her sunniest "Hi."

Cut.

EXTERIOR, HAVEN HAMILTON ESTATE, DAY.

The Tricycle Man motors his way along a gravel road that leads to Haven Hamilton's rambling log estate, situated in one of the more picturesque tree-filled knolls of Nashville. Behind him we see Opal and Albequerque, who is speaking into the tape recorder over the roar of the bike. A party is in progress and Lady Pearl (in pink today) announces their arrival from a side patio.

LADY PEARL
Holy dogshit! Will you look at that! Must be some friends of Buddy's.

Linnea on the terrace, comments to a woman nearby.

                              LINNEA
            Ever since that ol' **Easy Rider** movie, that's the kind of
            bike that everybody's been driving. Those long, low,
            laid-back in the front.

                              WOMAN
            They're so dangerous, aren't they?

                              LINNEA
            They are. Over there at the Baptist hospital, there's a
            whole ward full of the cutest, best lookin' boys you'd
            ever want to see, just paralyzed from the waist down.

Opal disembarks from the bike with all of her gear and
grandly thanks the motorcycle man, calling him ''da—ling.''
She tells Albequerque, in yesterday's clothes and newly-torn
nylons, to break a leg and leaves them all behind as she goes
off to trench in with Bud, who steps forward to greet her. She
gives him a show-biz kiss.

                              OPAL
            Well, well, well, young Hamilton!

                              BUD
            Fine, come on in.

                              OPAL
            Is your dad around? I'd like to have a little chat with
            him.

                              BUD
            Well, he's kinda tied up right now. . . maybe later.

                              OPAL
            Is your mom around?

                              BUD
            No, as a matter of fact, my mom's in Paris right now.

They walk past Albequerque, Opal not seeing her at all, as
Albequerque heads for the table where Wade stands serving
food and proceeds to load a paper plate with baked beans
until it collapses. Opal looks at the **Cries and Whispers**
surroundings.

                              OPAL
            This is Bergman.

                              BUD
            I like it here so much. It's kinda nice. Dad—

OPAL
Pure unadulterated Bergman! It's so beau — ti — ful. Do you live here?

BUD
We do. We been here for quite a while, I guess.

OPAL
It's beautiful. It's so gorgeous. Of course, the people are all wrong for Bergman, aren't they?

They sit on the edge of a stone wishing well.

BUD (not sure of what she's talking about)
Oh, yeah...

Off around the other end of the house, Lady Pearl and Haven talk to Triplette.

LADY PEARL
Haven breeds those famous Tennessee Walkers you've heard about.

TRIPLETTE
Oh, really?

HAVEN
Oh, Mr. Triplette, he knows all about Walkers.

John laughs politely.

LADY PEARL
That's not the kind of Walker I had in mind.

TRIPLETTE
That's very fast.

HAVEN (laughing politely back)
Yeah, we have to be.

On the terrace, Linnea is still into hospitals.

LINNEA
Well, she had this most horrible accident...a...she got a lick on the head, you know, getting into one of those tiny little cars, her daughter's car and this happened almost a year ago and no one had any idea that this was gonna develop into such a horrible thing.

Lady Pearl continues around the corner.

LADY PEARL
Now, I'm real sorry old Delbert went and told you that Haven would appear at the political rally. He knows better than that. We never let Haven Hamilton take sides politically.

Haven interrupts.

HAVEN

Understand, we give contributions to everybody, and they are not puny contributions.

LADY PEARL

Only time I ever went hog-wild and round the bend was for the Kennedy boys. But they were different.

TRIPLETTE

Oh yes, ma'am, yes ma'am, they were.

For a moment, Triplette's looks take on a number of Kennedy characteristics. A large black limousine drives up as Pearl excuses herself and Haven accepts a glass of milk from one of the maids. Norman is at the wheel. We hear the conversation between Haven's public relations girl, Sue Barton, and another of her clients, Elliott Gould.

SUE

Haven's singing at the Grand Old Opry and this is just a sort of preparty. I'm sure you've seen Haven Hamilton.

GOULD

No, I never heard of him.

SUE

He's been a country western star.

Norman, running to open the door for them is late, so he interrupts as they step out of the car.

NORMAN

Lemme get that . . . oh, well listen, I wanted to ask Mr. Gould . . .

Gould and she wait for his question.

Would it be alright if I asked him . . .

GOULD

You want to ask me something?

NORMAN

Yeah.

SUE

Well, we'll be riding back with you, Norman. Could we wait until then?

GOULD

Okay. Whatever you want.

NORMAN

I just wanted to know what you were doing here in

Nashville.

GOULD
I'm just coming to a party. What are you doing here in Nashville?

NORMAN (scratches his head & wonders)
Well, I'm stuck here . . a . . . I'm

SUE
See you in a bit, Norman.

They walk down into the party where someone asks Gould if he's making a film.

GOULD
No, I'm promoting a movie, not making one.

GIRL
Are you a personal friend of . . .

GOULD (interrrupting)
Oh yeah, we're very good friends.

Albequerque is seated on the ground near a tree. Wade comes over to her.

WADE
What're you doin' here anyway?

ALBEQUERQUE
Um . . . I came on a date and now I'm going to the grand Ole Opry.

He knows she is lying.

WADE
How?

ALBEQUERQUE
How?

WADE
Yeah — is your date gonna take you?

She looks around.

ALBEQUERQUE
Huh? . . . a . . . no, he, they left.

Opal still sits on the wishing well talking with Bud, only now she holds a mike.

BUD
No, I'm not a singer. I'm a businessman. I take care of all Dad's business.

OPAL (shocked)

You, a businessman?

BUD

Yeah.

OPAL (laughing)

With that face? You can't be a businessman.

BUD

Oh yeah! All his business, records, you know, anything that comes in through the...

OPAL

Do you like it?

BUD (lying)

Oh yeah, it's great. It really is. You know, Dad's wanted me to do that all his life.

On the patio, Haven listens to Triplette's calculated sell.

TRIPLETTE

Haven, listen, I'd be the last guy in the world to try and change your mind about something you don't want to do, but I'd like to explain a couple of things we're trying to do in this campaign before you discount it altogether.

Linnea continues with the details of her aunt.

LINNEA

And somehow the blood began to drain into behind her eyeball, you know, and the pressure just caused the eye to bulge out.

WOMAN

Ohh...

LINNEA

And it was all red and just looked awful. Everybody thought she was gonna lose her eye. We still don't know how it's gonna come out.

Triplette reinforces his sell.

TRIPLETTE

I don't know how you're gonna feel about this, but Walker thinks you'd make a fine governor in this state. He thinks the time's right. He thinks the people of Nashville love you. He knows they do. Knows how you feel about them. And he wants you to know should the time come and you want to run, he'll be there

with his organization to back you all the way.
Haven lets all that settle in for a moment before he answers.

                    HAVEN
You gonna be at the Opry tonight?

                    TRIPLETTE
Well, I hadn't thought...

                    HAVEN
Well, I'm gonna be at the Opry tonight.

                    TRIPLETTE
Oh, well sure, then I'll...

                    HAVEN (smiling)
Yes, I guess you will. And that's when I'll give you my
decision.

                    TRIPLETTE
Thanks so much for thinking about it.
Sue Barton has been introducing Elliott Gould around, and
now sends Delbert over to see if it's all right to meet Haven.
Opal, on her wishing well perch, raises Bud's chin with her
finger.

                    OPAL
You want to sing? Look at me.

                    BUD
Oh, I...

                    OPAL
Look at me!

                    BUD
I think everybody... Dad wouldn't hear of it. He really
wouldn't, he —

                    OPAL
But you want to be —
Delbert conveys his message to Haven.

                    TRIPLETTE
I know him; it's Elliott Gould. He's a very well known
actor.

                    DEL
Who —

                    HAVEN
Oh yes. Elliott, with the curly hair.

DEL

Yeah. . .

TRIPLETTE

Yeah. He was married to, uh. . . Barbra Streisand
and. . .

DEL

You're kidding me.

TRIPLETTE

. . . that girl that sang "People."

DEL (embarrassed)

I just shook the man's hand like he was somebody on
the street.

HAVEN

Delbert, now look, you go over there and bring him
on over.

DEL

Yes, sir, I'll. . .

TRIPLETTE (laughing)

We all walk down the street, Delbert.

Delbert walks to Gould and takes him warmly by the hand.

DEL

Listen, you all come over here. Haven wants to meet
you right away. I'm so sorry. . I didn't realize who you
were when we were first introduced.

GOULD (getting him off the hook)

Oh yeah? Well, I ain't changed.

Opal continues her investigation of Bud.

OPAL

You wrote a song?

BUD

Yeah, I wrote one song in my life.

OPAL (gently)

I'd like to hear it.

BUD

You sure?

She gives him her softest eyes and her fullest attention.

OPAL

Um humm.

BUD

Okay.

He begins to sing softly so no one will hear. It's a sweet, sincere song, and Opal soaks it in like a sponge. She turns and faces the party for the first time in a while. Somewhere around "it comes from the heart of a gentle woman", she sees Gould go around the corner to meet Haven.

The sound of her hello soft and tenderly,
The way she lights my morning with a smile,
And when she says I need you, oh, I need you,
It makes my life so worthwhile —
'Cause it comes from the heart of a gentle woman.
It comes from the soul of an angel from above.
And I'll stay in the heart of a gentle . . .

OPAL (squealing),

Elliott Gould! Why . . it's Elliott Gould!
She bends over and picks up her equipment with nary a look back to Bud, who's sorry he ever began in the first place. Elliott approaches with Sue.

LADY PEARL

Well, let me meet the movie star!

SUE

Lady Pearl . . .

LADY PEARL (she gives his hand a handshake)
Howdy.

GOULD

Lady Pearl . .

SUE

Haven Hamilton.

HAVEN (they shake hands)
Well, how do you do, Mr. Gould? It's so nice to meet you, and welcome to Nashville and my lovely home.
From around the corner comes Opal with her microphone extended and shouting —

OPAL	GOULD
Elliott! Elliott! Elliott Gould!!!	Oh, hello.

OPAL

Hello.

GOULD

Oh, just a...

HAVEN

What brings you here?

Gould stands caught between the two currents.

OPAL

How are you? You look
marvelous! It's Opal from
the BBC. Don't you
remember... the Cannes
Film Festival? Well, no, of
course you wouldn't
remember. How silly of
me.

HAVEN

Sue, another unexpected
guest. You can't do that to
me twice in one day. Is
she connected to Mr.
Gould?

SUE

No, she's not.

GOULD

I'm not giving any interviews.

OPAL

What are you doing in
Nashville? What am I
doing in Nashville is more
like it.

HAVEN

Well, in that case, we're
not and I'm not going to
permit·her to stay here.

SUE (to Opal)

Excuse me.

OPAL

I'm doing a documentary...

SUE

Excuse me, but Mr. Gould does not give interviews.

OPAL

My machine's not on! Mr.
Gould happens to be a
friend of mine. Mr.
Hamilton! My machine is
not on.

HAVEN (interrupting
roughly)

I don't know who you are
or what you're doing
here, but I will not
tolerate rudeness in the
presence of a star — two
stars. Delbert, would you
take her? Thank you so
very much. So nice, that's
right, good-bye.

Del puts his arm around Opal and cheerfully leads her off in another direction.

DEL
Listen, it's gonna be all right.

Opal looks at him as if he were a bug.

OPAL
Who are you?

We hold on Haven and Gould for just a moment as Haven smiles.

HAVEN
Well, that's the price of success, I guess.

And Gould smiles back.

GOULD
It certainly is.

Cut.

EXTERIOR COUNTRY ROAD, DAY.

The Tricycle Man drives through a patch of trees and onto the highway past a red, white and blue sign that reads "Connie White, Haven Hamilton, Tommy Brown — Home of Country Music — Opryland USA." In the background we hear the theme music for WSM radio's **Grand Old Opry**.

ANNOUNCER
Go get a Goo-Goo, friends, and settle back for thirty of the goodest minutes in radio...

INTERIOR, GRAND OLD OPRY, DAY.

We see an audience, packed in floor to ceiling, before a red velvet curtain which raises, revealing the musicians playing onstage and the announcer, who stands at the podium.

ANNOUNCER
...the Grand Old Opry, and it's sent your way by the makers of Goo-Goo, the goodest candy bar in the world. And King Leo pure stick candy, the candy that roars with flavor

We see Tommy Brown, his wife, family and friends standing backstage.

ANNOUNCER
Now a big welcome if you please for the Goo-Goo man of the hour — Tommy Brown!

The announcer signals the audience to applaud as the music comes up and Tommy walks out onstage. His family go and sit in the historic church pews, from Ryman Auditorium, also

onstage behind the band and in front of the painted red barn backdrop. The Goo Goo cluster poster, painted on the top of the backdrop, is also from the old Ryman Auditorium.

As Tommy sings, the audience claps time. They walk down the aisles with cameras to take his picture or drift back and forth to the popcorn stands on either side of the auditorium. Most of the spectators are from out of state and have planned this trip months in advance to see their radio favorites. They are as dedicated a group as you will find anywhere.

BROWN (singing)
I've been going down that long lonesome road, babe,
And I've been doing it for a while,
Yeah, I've been going down that long lonesome road babe,
Looking for a special smile,
Now I work the bars from New York to Frisco,
But I could never make it pay—
You know how money goes,
It slips right through your fingers,
One more dollar one more day. . . .

Cut.

EXERIOR, ENTRANCE, OPRY, NIGHT.
We see Wade's truck drive up, stop at the backstage entrance to the Opry, and deposit Albequerque. Jean Shepard's show bus stands in the parking lot.

WADE
This is as far as I'm taking you. I don't know how you're gonna get in.

ALBEQUERQUE
Don't worry about me.
She gets out of the car and walks down the passageway with great authority. She pats the striped awning above her.

ALBEQUERQUE
This here's the new one, all right.

Cut.

INTERIOR, AUDIENCE, NIGHT.
Tommy continues to sing as we look through the audience and find the Tricycle Man on one side, L. A. Joan in gold sequins

sitting next to Pvt. Kelly on another, Kenny eating popcorn and sipping a Coke in still another section of the audience, and walking down one aisle and up another we see Star scanning the audience for a glimpse of Albequerque.

INTERIOR, BACKSTAGE ENTRANCE, OPRY, NIGHT.

Delbert and Opal enter as Albequerque is trying to lie her way in, and when Delbert says "She's with me," meaning Opal, Albequerque seizes her good fortune and sails in, too. Tommy Brown's song comes to an end.

Cut.

INTERIOR, OPRY AUDIENCE, NIGHT.

Now the announcer and another man, who puts on his glasses, stand at the podium and read the following commercial.

ANNOUNCER

Thank you, Tommy. Beautiful job as always. Say, Harold Weakly — have you been on vacation yet?

HAROLD

Gosh, no, I been busier than a puppy in a room full of rubber balls.

ANNOUNCER

And if you're like me, all that hustling and bustling makes you want to sit down and let the world go by while you enjoy a Goo-Goo candy cluster.

INTERIOR, BACKSTAGE OPRY.

A yellow-shirted guard stands at the entrance of the stage. Delbert nods his way through with Opal on his arm. As Albequerque starts through, the guard stops her.

GUARD

Hello, can I help you?

ALBEQUERQUE

Oh, I'm with these people here.

GUARD

Do you have a backstage pass?

ALBEQUERQUE

A pass?

GUARD

Yes, ma'am.

ALBEQUERQUE

They didn't need a pass.

GUARD

You need a pass to get backstage.

Cut.

INTERIOR, SUELEEN GAY'S ROOM, DAY.

A whole Jesus, Mary, and Joseph crèche sits next to a hair dryer, an array of dime store make-up, a live gold fish, a stuffed frog, card pictures of some more saints, and one or two pictures of Sueleen lean on the playing radio atop her dresser. In the mirror we see Sueleen in blue rollers and a pale green kimona shaking her bosoms as she sings through the commercial.

SUELEEN (singing)	ANNOUNCER
Even if we stay together	A Goo-Goo's the perfect
Our whole lifetime	answer when you need a
through,	quick pick up — Go get a
I'll never get enough,	Goo-Goo, the South's
I'll never get enough,	favorite piece of candy
I'll never get enough,	for sixty-two years.
Of you.	

She does several bumps, none of which please her, so she starts in again.

Cut.

INTERIOR, OPRY STAGE, DAY.

ANNOUNCER

Ready to do the song?

HAROLD

Right.

ANNOUNCER

Okay.

And they sing.

Go get a Goo-Goo — it's good.

The Goo-Goo sign lights up and the audience applauds. Behind the announcer's curtain, Tommy passes Haven and his entourage in the wings and smiles, saying:

BROWN

I don't know about killin' them, Haven, they're already dead.

HAVEN (smiling back)

Yeah. He's lucky to be alive.

Mr. Nashville himself. . . HAVEN — HAMILTON!
The audience bursts into applause as Haven walks out, both
arms raised to the mass of faces who feel he is their own
somehow. He thanks them and proceeds.

HAVEN
And I'm sure you meant to share that welcome with
Bud Hamilton, my son, who's here. Stand up, Bud.
Everyone applauds as Bud rises and nods from the packed pew
including Pearl, Sue Barton, Delbert and Triplette, not to men-
tion two oogling girls who sit behind Bud.

HAVEN
Ain't he somethin' else? Yes, indeed. God bless you. I
thank you for that warm welcome. I'd like to do a
brand-new song. . .
In the pew, Triplette whispers to Del.

TRIPLETTE
How tall is that guy?

DEL
Who?

TRIPLETTE (laughing)
Haven.

DEL (also laughing)
Don't ever ask him that.
And as Opal creeps around taking pictures, Haven sings and
the audience applauds, as led by the announcer.

HAVEN
Unpack your bags an' try not to cry.
I can't leave my wife; there's three reasons why. There's
Jimmy, an Kathy and sweet Lorelei.
For the sake of the children, we must say good-bye.

INTERIOR, BACKSTAGE.
Albequerque still stands holding her ground as the guard
continues to hold her. She turns and spots Connie White, an ash-
blonde, kitten face in a red tulle dress. Her torso looks like a
heart shaped box of chocolates. Connie's rise to stardom has
been apart from the camaraderie of discovery. She wrote
some songs and pedaled them any way she could until finally
one of them emerged as a hit. In the performing community,
she is a bit of a loner, devoting her time to her mother and her
work. She gives little time to things that interfere with work.

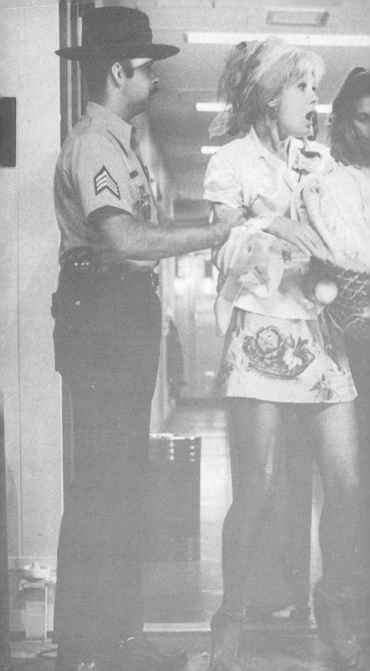

ALBEQUERQUE
Oh! There's Connie
White!

Connie smiles one of her
fixed smiles.

CONNIE
Hi ya, honey.

Albequerque, still
struggling with the guard,
tries to become Connie's
best friend.

ALBEQUERQUE
Hi ya. Listen, you
know what? You
remember you
signed my album?

Connie presses on.

CONNIE
Well, thank you for
comin', dear. Thank
you for comin' to the
show.

She crosses behind the
guard and gives him her
best "get rid of her"
smile.

ALBEQUERQUE
I have a song I wrote
and I'll give you a
call tomorrow, okay?

CONNIE (dismissing her)
That's fine, dear.

ALBEQUERQUE
You know 'cause
we'll just chat, you
know—

Connie starts to move
toward the stage.

HAVEN
'Cause Jimmy's
been wishing
That I'd take him
fishing.
His little-league
pitching
Is something to see.
Kathy's thirteen now,
She's my little queen
now,
And I've gotta see
Who her beau's
gonna be.
So unpack your bags
And try not to cry.
I can't leave my
wife;
There's three reasons
why. . .
There's Jimmy and
Kathy and sweet
Lorelei.
For the sake of the
children
We must say good-
bye,
'Cause Laurie's just
walking,
She just started
talking, And Daddy's
the first word
that she ever heard.
So unpack your bags
And try not to cry.
I can't leave my
wife;
There's three reasons
why.

CONNIE

Do you remember what I wrote on the program? Do you remember?

ALBEQUERQUE

Yeah. You said, "You were my friend — Connie White."

Connie pats her hand and sails off followed by her manager and hairdresser.

There's Jimmy and Kathy
And sweet Lorelei.
For the sake of the children
We must say good-bye.
For the sake of the children
We must say good-bye.

We hear applause in the background.

CONNIE

That's right, "Your friend — Connie White."

The guard tightens his grip as Albequerque continues:

ALBEQUERQUE

I like your dress. I'm gonna get one, too. But you know I like the gold one with the . . . you know, the belt . . . you look like you have no waist. . . .

INTERIOR, STAGE.

As Haven announces his next song, Star gives the audience another go round, passing the Tricycle Man first, then Kenny. As he does, Triplette checks out the back of Haven's shirt.

TRIPLETTE

He's got the entire galaxy on the back of his shirt.

Del chuckles. It's true; the sun, moon and stars glitter across Haven's frame as he sings:

HAVEN

Ain't no use to sit and whine,
'Cause the fish ain't on your line.
Bait your hook and keep on trying,
Keep a-goin'.

As Star goes down the center aisle, we see L. A. Joan and Pvt. Kelly for a moment. In the wings, Connie petulantly primps, and grabs off quick smiles for photographers.

Cut.

INTERIOR, BARBARA-JEAN'S HOSPITAL ROOM, DAY.

Barnett sits fiddling with the radio and finishing his second box of Kentucky fried chicken, while Barbara-Jean sits on the bed painting her nails with clear polish. There are still more flowers in the room and they seem to take the air away. We hear Haven's voice on the radio.

> **HAVEN**
>
> And if the doctor says you're through,
> Keep a-goin'.
> Why, he's a human being just like you
> Keep a-goin'.
> Ain't no law says you must die;
> Wipe them tears from off your eye;
> Give the world another try;
> Keep a-goin'.

INTERIOR, STAGE, GRAND OLD OPRY, DAY.

Haven finishes his last "Keep A-Goin' " with a "Yes, sir," that gets swallowed up in the applause.

> **HAVEN**
>
> Thank you, and God love you. Course we wanta send very special greetings to our own Barbara-Jean. I know most of you read she collapsed out at the airport. She's in Vanderbilt Hospital recuperating and Barnett tells me she cried real tears because she couldn't be here tonight. So, I hope you'll send some letters and best wishes and prayers to her, Vanderbilt Hospital — Nashville, Tennessee 27322, and tell her Haven told you to write. Now as a special stand-in for her we have her dear friend Connie White, who got out of the dentist's chair this morning where she was having some root canal work done and came all the way out here to sing for you. Miss Connie White, friend of yours and mine, and a wonderful singer in her own way — Connie White.

As Connie sweeps out in a flurry of red tulle, Pvt. Kelly gets up, excuses himself from a startled L. A. Joan, and leaves. No one can replace Barbara-Jean for him. Connie's on-stage entourage exchanges places with Haven's, and when Triplette gets to the wings he whispers to Del again.

> **TRIPLETTE**
>
> I haven't seen a dress like that since the junior prom.

                    DEL (laughing)
Yeah...
                    TRIPLETTE
    My date fell out of the car.
Connie is downstage talking to a cluster of children at the
footlights. Several of them say their names and ages into the
microphone. Connie signs autographs and gives a word of
advice before she starts singing.
                    CONNIE
    I want you to study real hard because just remember:
    anyone of you can grow up to be the president.
Someone in the audience applauds; we see Kenny for just a
moment and then her song begins.
                    CONNIE
    Well, I'd like to go to Memphis
    But I don't know the way
    And I'd like to tell you how I feel
    But I don't know what to say.
    And I'd love to go to heaven
    But I forgot how to pray.
    So just help me keep from sliding down some
    more...
    Well, I'd like to give you all I got,
    But I don't know what that is.
    And I'd like to take you with me,
    But I don't know where that is.
    And I know there must be somethin' some place
    And some way to live.
    So just help me keep from slidin' down some more...
    Just help me keep from slidin' down some more...
    Some more...
She bows and seques into the next tune, I know you love me.
                                                Cut.
INTERIOR, BARBARA-JEAN'S HOSPITAL ROOM, DAY.
Barnett is now into the apple turnover, and Barbara-Jean
gives her nails a second coat as Connie's voice fills the room
with her song. Finally, Barbara-Jean has had enough.
                    BARBARA-JEAN
    Turn that off.
                    BARNETT
    Okay, one more minute, darlin'.

BARBARA-JEAN
Right now!

BARNETT
Honey, she'll be through with the song in a moment, right?

BARBARA-JEAN
I want you to turn it off right now! It bothers me.

BARNETT
It bothers me too, but I got to listen to her, don't I?

BARBARA-JEAN
Why?

BARNETT
Come on now. Gotta go over to The King of the Road and thank her personal-like for you, don't I?

BARBARA-JEAN
Thank her?

BARNETT
I gotta know what song she sang, don't I?

BARBARA-JEAN
You can ask anybody. You can call. You can send flowers. You can send a message—

BARNETT
Oh, come on, don't get upset.

BARBARA-JEAN
You're makin' me ruin my nail polish job.

BARNETT
Do I tell you how to sing, darlin'? Hmm? Have I ever told you how to sing a song?

BARBARA-JEAN
That ain't the point. Goin' over there...

BARNETT
Don't tell me how to promote.

BARBARA-JEAN
I know why you're goin' over there.

BARNETT
Don't tell me how to run your life, I've been doin' pretty good with it.

BARBARA-JEAN

You do, uh; well...

BARNETT

All right, let's just calm down; we're both getting on each other's nerves.

BARBARA-JEAN

You're goin' over to King of the Road and I know why. So you can hobnob with everybody.

BARNETT

So I can do what?

BARBARA-JEAN

And I ain't got no friends; I got to sit here in this...

BARNETT

So I can hobnob?

BARBARA-JEAN

... goddam hospital and they're all gonna talk about..

BARNETT

I don't even like the word hobnob; I ain't doing no hobnobbin'.

BARBARA-JEAN

... how I'm a nut!

BARNETT (turning off radio)

Ho, ho, ho, now...

BARBARA-JEAN

And how I got a...I had... Barbara-Jean had another collapse.

She changes course midsentence.

You know what? While you're at it, why don't you take some flowers? You can take her some of my flowers.

She gets up off the bed, picks up a yellow mum wreath with black ribbons and plops it down near Barnett.

BARBARA-JEAN

Why don't you take her this nice black one? That'll cheer her up.

BARNETT

Are you through?

BARBARA-JEAN

No, I ain't through!

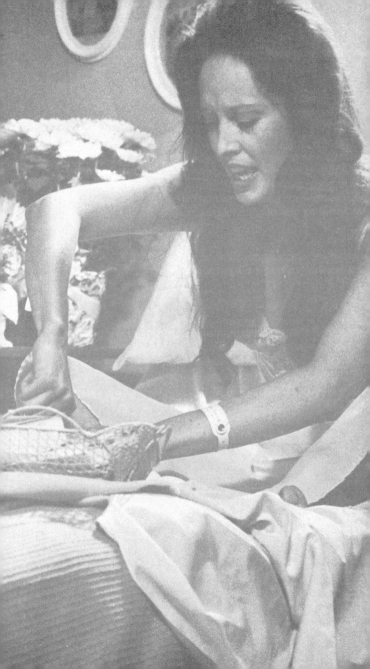

She picks up a bouquet of carnations and plops them down on the table next to Barnett.

BARNETT

Are you through!

BARBARA-JEAN

And these — why don't you try these?

She comes twice more with flowers and bangs them down on the table next to Barnett. The last bouquet she throws on the floor, breaking the container, spilling water and flowers everywhere. Barnett, having lost patience, stands shouting.

BARNETT

Are you through, I said.

Barbara-Jean drops to the floor at the foot of the bed and begins to tremble, holding her head in her hands. Barnett kneels beside her.

BARNETT

Are you goin' nutsy on me; is that what you're doing? 'Cause I won't stand for that, Barbara-Jean huh? You having one of them nervous breakdowns? Huh?

She raises her head and shakes her head no.

BARBARA-JEAN

No, no...

BARNETT

Well, you coulda fooled me, 'cause it looks like you're ready for it. Now you just settle down and shape up, you understand? The only reason I'm going over there is 'cause I love **you.** I don't love to go over there and hobnob with them phonies.

Barnett dissolves for just a moment, making one wonder who is really in control.

BARNETT

Why do you make me raise my voice to you? Huh? Why do you put us through this?

She begins to sob.

You all right?

Unwilling to let her get too far into crying, he takes her hand as he cajoles.

BARNETT

Come on, honey, let's have a little smile for Barnett.

B.J. (crying)

I'm tired of this place —

He starts to rise, bringing her up with him.

BARNETT

Come on—come on, now, get up. You help me and I'll help you, all right? Come on, now...come on, now.

She is up, drops his hand, and walks zombie-like to her bed.

BARNETT

Now, where's Barnett going? Where am I going? Hmm?

B.J. (barely whispers)

King of the Road...

BARNETT

And why am I goin' there?

B.J. (barely whispers)

To see Connie...

BARNETT

And why am I doing that?

BARBARA-JEAN

Thank her for singin' for me...

BARNETT

Now who am I doin' that for?

B.J. (like a puppet)

Doin' it for me...

BARNETT

That's right.

She sits on the bed and can't stop crying but tries to. Barnett tries to believe he's doing the right thing and they are caught in real time acting out a fantasy.

BARNETT (smiles cheerfully)

Now, I'm walking out now.

BARBARA-JEAN

Um huh.

BARNETT (as to a child)

Now, what do you say when I walk out? You say "bye-bye."

Barbara-Jean mimics him, barely able to get it out.

B.J. (softly)

Bye.

BARNETT

Bye-bye.

BARBARA-JEAN

    Bye.

The door closes and he is gone. Barbara-Jean holds on to herself for a minute, as if to not lose any more than she already has. Then, fearful that he might really leave her, she calls out.

BARBARA-JEAN

    Barnett? . . . Barnett!

But it's too late, as he's off to execute his errand of good-will.

Cut. 1

INTERIOR, NGHTCLUB, NIGHT.

Inside the King of the Road, we see at a long row of small tables Haven, Connie, their respective entourages, Opal talking to Lady Pearl, Delbert and Triplette. Vassar Clemens is playing his fiddle onstage, and at another table in the corner Bill sits with Norman, waiting for Mary.

BILL

    I'm really upset.

NORMAN

What're you upset about?

BILL

    She's really late.

NORMAN (looks at his watch)

Hell, she's not that late.

BILL

    No, she's late.

In the doorway we see Sue Barton, the P. R. girl, with a young, tousled-looking woman. Sue leads her to Haven, who has just said "Thank you so much" for the nine-hundredth time this evening. Sue leans down, whispers in his ear and he stands.

SUE

    I'd like you to meet Julie Christie.

HAVEN

    Well, it's so nice to see you. Welcome to Nashville.

Julie smiles, lighting everything up around her except Opal and Lady Pearl, engaged in a conversation so intense that Opal doesn't even see Julie.

JULIE
Hello.

Everyone nearby stands
up except Connie.

DEL (aside to Triplette)
Is she the one that
got off the train in
the snow?

HAVEN
Won't you sit down?

JULIE
Oh, no thanks.

SUE
This is Connie White.

CONNIE
Hi there.

Connie looks at Julie,
unable to find a frame of
reference for the way she
looks.

JULIE
Hello.

CONNIE (based on Julies
accent)
You're English, aren't
you?

JULIE
Unhuh.

HAVEN
Look at her. . . isn't
she lovely. This is
such a coincidence.

DEL (shaking her hand)
I'm Del Reese.

HAVEN
I was talkin' about
the Christie Minstrels
just this morning and
now we have Julie
Christie here. . .

OPAL
Oh, a Hal Phillip
Walker button — no,
it's Kennedy. Isn't it
rather ancient? I
thought everyone in
the South didn't go
for Kennedy.

LADY PEARL
John Fitzgerald
Kennedy, he took
the whole South
except for
Tennessee,
Kentucky, and
there's a reason he
didn't take
Tennessee. But he
got 481, 450 votes
and the asshole got
556, 577 votes.

Panning past Opal's
interest, we see Bill and
Norman again.

BILL
I can just tell. There's
something in the
way she looks at
me. It's that feeling
you get that you
know something
"else's" going on.

NORMAN
No. . .

Lady Pearl picks up
again.

TRIPLETTE
Hi. We met at Peter Finch's.

JULIE
Oh, yeah?

HAVEN
Won't you sit down?

SUE
No, Julie has a friend who's playing at the Exit Inn. We just stopped in to say hello.

HAVEN
Well, I hope your stay here is very nice and I hope you'll remember what film facilities we have here in Nashville.

JULIE
Oh, yes. Sure. Good-bye.
Everyone says good-bye as they leave, and resume their seats.

HAVEN
Well, isn't that an honor. What a surprise! Julie Christie.

CONNIE
Who's she?

LADY PEARL
Well, now the problem we got here is anti-Catholicism. These dumbheads around here, they're all Baptists and whatever, I dunno. Even to teach 'em to make change over the bar ya gotta crack their skulls. Let alone teach 'em to vote for Kennedy, because he happens to be the better man. Then, I don't remember the next few days were...I just remember that T.V. set on an' seeing it all. Seeing that fat-bellied sheriff sayin', "Ruby, you sonofabitch." And Oswald and her in her little pink suit.
Lady Pearl begins to cry and Opal looks around uncomfortably.

HAVEN
You know, Julie Christie, she's a famous star. She got one of those Academy Awards.

CONNIE (shocked)
No!

HAVEN

Yes, I'm not kidding. She got it for one of those pictures. I don't know which one, she's done so many.

CONNIE (laughing)

Isn't he awful? Haven's got the worst sense of humor.

HAVEN

No, she's lovely, just a beautiful girl.

CONNIE

Come on, Haven, she can't even comb her hair.

Barnett comes through the door carrying a single orchid corsage wrapped in cellophane, and makes his way to Haven's table where someone says, "Look who's here." There is no chair and no one offers to get him one, so he stands uncomfortably behind Connie as Vassar finishes playing and the applause begins.

CONNIE (dimly)

Hi, Barnett.

BARNETT (politely)

How are you, Connie?

He extends the flower, which she ignores.

It's just a little something that Barbara-Jean told me to pick up for you.

CONNIE

Oh, Barnett, you shouldn't have done that.

BARNETT	VASSAR
I know I shouldn't have, but she told me; I told her I shouldn't have.	Thank you, thank you very much. And as most of you might've already noticed, we have a celebrity in the house with us tonight. And if we can put our hands together, we might be able to get a song.
He laughs, trying to make a joke of the whole thing.	
CONNIE'S MANAGER	
Did you get the flowers we sent to you?	

There is applause and cheers. Haven starts to rise.

VASSAR

Miss Connie White!

Haven changes gears quickly and turns to Connie, who reacts to the unexpected announcement with surprise and then poise. As she leaves, Barnett and his corsage sit down in her chair. Connie makes her way to the stage and begins to sing "Rolling Stone." Lady Pearl tearfully begins again with Opal.

DELBERT
That was a nice gesture.

BARNETT
Hmm?

DELBERT
A nice gesture.

BARNETT
What was a nice gesture?

DELBERT
Bringing that. Barnett looks around for a moment.

BARNETT
But it don't seem to be appreciated, do it?

LADY PEARL
And then comes Bobby. Well, I worked for him... I worked here... Opal interrupts partly because she doesn't want her to cry again and partly because she has her own feelings about Bobby.

OPAL
A... don't you think that... Lady Pearl hasn't heard. She continues with the recreation as the song continues in the background.

LADY PEARL
I worked all over the country. I worked in California, out in Stockton where Bobby came. He came here and spoke and went down to Memphis, and when he went out to Stockton, California, he spoke off the Santa Fe train at the old Santa Fe depot.
Opal looks around for a way out, but she can't find one.

LADY PEARL (tearfully)
Oh! He was a beautiful man. He... was not much like, uh, John, you know; he was more — puny-like. But all the time I was workin' for him, I was so scared, inside, y'know? So scared.
At the other end of the table, Barnett sits in defensive verbal combat with a member of Connie's coterie. The song continues and Triplette leans into Haven.

TRIPLETTE
Haven, you think we can get Connie out to the rally, too?

Haven smiles and leans back.

HAVEN
Connie White and Barbara-Jean never appear on the same stage together. Connie might replace Barbara-Jean but that's it.

Then he smiles and adds:

HAVEN
And as for Haven Hamilton, well—I'll appear wherever Barbara-Jean appears.

He leans back and takes a drink of milk as Triplette nods to himself and says resignedly.

TRIPLETTE
Okay.

Across the table, Barnett storms on.

BARNETT
I got a good mind to take you outside. With my wife in the hospital, you puttin' that shit on me?

Connie's manager, who perhaps provoked the outburst, wraps it up.

CONNIE'S MANAGER
Calm down, Barnett. Calm down and enjoy the show.

Right or wrong who knows, but for Triplette this is just another indication that his job will not be easy. Somewhere behind Triplette, Bill continues to wait for Mary as Connie sings.

CONNIE (sings)	BILL
Walk with me, Joshua, And I'll say that I am lame. I'll have, sweet Joshua, That child that we have made. But I'll never let him mention Your name. Rolling stone, rolling stone gathers no moss, But neither does it gather Any love.	I. . . I think she's. . . uh having an affair here.
	Norman is a little bleary with tequila, but definite:
	NORMAN
	Oh God, are you off. You're way off.
	BILL
	No.
	NORMAN
	You are way, way off. Are you kidding?
	Cut.

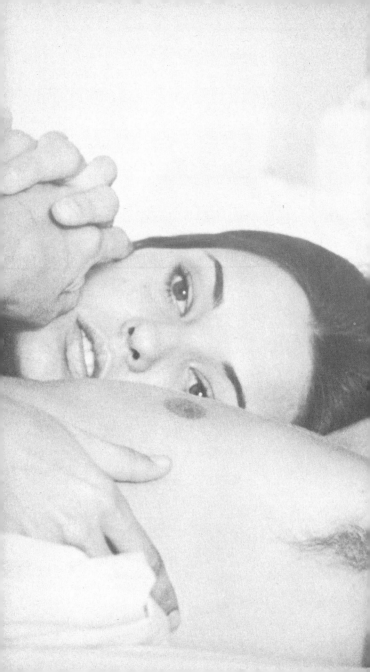

INTERIOR, TOM'S MOTEL ROOM, NIGHT.

Starting with the turning spools, we hear Tom's voice on the tape singing, pan down to a clump of clothes on the floor, then across to the bed where two pairs of feet stick out at the bottom. Continuing the pan, we see Mary tucked in Tom's arm. He is asleep, she is not, and she quietly tells him what she could never tell him if he were awake.

> MARY
>
> I love you...

> MARY
>
> I love you...

> MARY
>
> I love you...

> TOM (on taped song)
> Some people take
> and never give.
> All men die; some
> must live.
> And life is short, a
> precious gift,
> This thing we have —
> Please don't let it
> drift away.
> Honey, won't you
> Let me be your
> friend?
> Honey, won't you let
> me try again?
> Honey, won't you let
> me be your friend,
> For another day?

And she looks up at him, wishing the song were true.

Cut.

SUNDAY.

INTERIOR, CATHOLIC CHURCH, DAY.

Christ on a stained glass window looks down on us and the

singing choir in the balcony, which includes Sueleen Gay.
Spread out through the rest of the singing congregation are
Star, Lady Pearl, and Wade.

Cut.

INTERIOR, PROTESTANT CHURCH, DAY.
Haven stands in the middle of his church choir. Off to the
side we see a woman conducting the hymn in sign
language for the deaf members of the congregation,
including Reese's children. Delbert stands beside his
children and we hold on Jimmy's sunny face for a moment
before we cut to:

INTERIOR, BLACK BAPTIST CHURCH, DAY.
A black minister and young girl stand knee deep in the
baptismal font. He performs the words to the ritual,
submerges her completely in the water, stands her back on
her feet, and says "Amen." The all black choir, including
Linnea break into song. Tommy Brown and his wife sing in
the congregation.

Cut.

INTERIOR, HOSPITAL CHAPEL, DAY.
Barbara-Jean is seated in a wheelchair singing "In the
Garden" to a small congregation of hospital inmates.
Pulling back, we see Barnett sitting in the first pew, and
further back Mr. Green sits next to Pvt. Kelly. At one point
Green turns and whispers to the soldier.

                    MR. GREEN
        You know, my wife, Esther, is on the same floor with
        Barbara-Jean.
Pvt. Kelly smiles and nods politely, caught completely up in
Barbara-Jean.

                    MR. GREEN
        Oh, a . . . Esther and I had a son in the service, too.

                    KELLY
        Yes, sir.

                    MR. GREEN
        Well, not in the army; he was in the navy.
Pvt. Kelly nods again.
        And . . . we lost him in the Pacific. We don't know how.

                    KELLY
        I'm sorry to hear that, sir.

                MR. GREEN (not hearing)
        World War Two, that's right.

Kelly nods to him reassuringly, as Barbara-Jean finishes the hymn.

KELLY

Yes, sir.

Cut.

EXTERIOR, JUNKYARD, DAY.

With Sunday church bells chiming behind her, Opal speaks oratorically into her machine. She walks through a graveyard of wrecked cars in multicolored, four-story-high stacks. She is insulated from the nearby freeway, the supply source for the wreckage on display.

OPAL

I'm wandering in a graveyard; the dead here have no crosses, nor tombstones, nor wreathes to sing of their past glory. But lie — in rotting — decaying, rusty heaps. Their innards ripped out by greedy, vulturous hands. Their vast, vacant skeletons sadly sighing to the sky. The rust on their bodies is the color of dried blood. Dried blood...I'm reminded of — of an elephant's secret burial ground. Yes. **Le val de mystère. C'est l'estompe de gloire.**

Kenny moves out of the wreckage gathering parts for his broken car. He watches Opal privately for a moment.

> OPAL
>
> These cars are trying to communicate. O cars, are you trying to tell me something?

> KENNY
>
What?

> OPAL
>
> Are you trying to convey to me some secret—

> KENNY
>
What?

Opal discovers she is not alone and walks over to Kenny.

> OPAL
>
> Oh! Excuse me. I thought I was completely alone here! How embarrassing.

Kenny picks up the pieces he's chosen and, with his violin case in hand, he starts to walk down the path away from the car graveyard telling her you can take the whole place for fifty cents. Opal follows quickly. Seeing the violin case, she says:

OPAL

Oh! You're a classical musician!

EXTERIOR, STOCK-CAR RACEWAY, DAY.

The high-pitched whine of a car revved up to full throttle connects with its image as it rounds the corner and comes down the grandstand stretch. In the infield, a talent show is in progress with a contestant singing "It Don't Worry Me." We can't hear, though, because the race is in progress. Also in the infield, we see cars being unloaded that bear the names of Haven Hamilton and Tommy Brown, who own them. The singer finishes, and next up to try for the $20 first prize is Albequerque, still wearing her small skirt and running hose. She makes her way to the microphone with Frog, while in the stands Haven prepares to give Tommy a large piece of water-melon from his picnic lunch. Lady Pearl intervenes, however, handing Tommy the grapes and Haven a look to kill. Mean-while, Albequerque has begun her song "with gestures," but she can't be heard. Between the car noise and the an-nouncer, it seems hopeless. We last see her, hands on hips, watching a gray car and Car #48 battle it out for first place.

Cut.

INTERIOR, BILL AND MARY'S HOTEL ROOM, DAY.

In his orange bathrobe, Bill sits on his dirty dish- and news-paper-covered bed, absently working out a chord on the guitar. Mary is in the other bed, back to him and buried under the covers. All that is visible is some dark hair. Through the window we see the Nashville skyline. Bill's anxiety gets the better of him and he begins to end the silence.

BILL

Do you want to talk about yesterday?

There is no answer.

BILL

Goddam it!

He has a lighted cigarette stuck in his guitar, which he uses to pop a balloon tied on her headboard.

Get up, goddam it!

Mary, in t-shirt and bobbie socks, gets up and thrashes out of bed, walks across his, stepping in the tray of dirty dishes, which crash into Bill.

MARY

Fucker!

She walks through the room and enters the bathroom, slam-ming the door behind her. Bill follows, banging on the door.

BILL

Do you want to talk about yesterday? (no response)
Shit! Come outa there.

She bangs back from inside.

MARY (yelling)

Leave me alone!

BILL

Come outa there! (He hits the door again) Look, I
know whats going... Come on!

She opens the door and comes out, crossing to a chest of
drawers. She pulls them out and dumps the contents into the
already debris-decorated space: old food, toys, recorders,
records, souvenirs... behind her, the TV set that is still on from
last night. She sits on the floor and picks through the clothes.

BILL

Oh that's terrific, great, that's just terrific.

She pushes the turtle stool out of the way.

BILL

Oh, thanks. My turtle, thanks a lot. Just relax, would
ya? Look, I know what's going on.

There is a knock at the door.

BILL

Oh great! House detective.

He goes to the door and opens it on Triplette in pale blue
Brooks Brothers.

TRIPLETTE

Bill, hi. I'm John Triplette. Am I early? I called you this
morning.

As Bill lets him in, Mary gets up, walks into the bedroom, and
shuts the door.

BILL

Oh, yeah. The guy from T.V. Come on in.

TRIPLETTE

Thank you.

Bill starts trying to clear a path.

BILL

Just... uh... cleaning up here.

TRIPLETTE (laughing)

Sunday morning blues.

BILL

Right. Uh, hold this for a second.

Bill hands him the turtle while he clears a spot on the purple couch.

TRIPLETTE (amiably)

Sure.

BILL

Just sit — over here.

Triplette sits packed next to the open guitar case and more, partially consumed, food and drink. He picks up an album.

TRIPLETTE

This is your new album?

BILL

Our **only** album.

TRIPLETTE

It's a very good one, though. I've heard it.

BILL

Oh, thank you.

TRIPLETTE

Terrific.

The fight lingers in the air.

BILL

Yeah.

He tosses some things from the chair to the floor.

BILL

I'm really sorry about the mess. We had a little party last night.

TRIPLETTE

Oh, that's all right. You oughta see my room.

And without further amenities:

I wanted to tell you a couple of things about what we're trying to do... this show.

BILL

Can I get you a drink?

TRIPLETTE

No, no, fine.

BILL

I could call downstairs.

TRIPLETTE

No, listen, I don't want to take up much of your time, (not really wanting to take up much of his). I just want

to tell you a little bit about what we're trying to do. I
know you're astute, politically, and I'm certainly not
here to sell you a bill of goods.

BILL

Don't care... don't care about politics.

TRIPLETTE

No politics.

BILL

No.

TRIPLETTE

Okay, great. Well, I've got a problem that I think could
work to your advantage. As you know, this
uh... redneck music is very popular right now and, uh,
I've got an awful lot of those local yokels on the bill,
y'know, singing...

BILL

Your basic country-folk...

TRIPLETTE

Crapola, right.

BILL

Right.

TRIPLETTE

I think — what I'm going for is a broader appeal, you
know —

BILL

Which is where we would fit in.

TRIPLETTE

More than just this, this Southern thing. And, uh, I think
that, you could really really hit — A group like yours
could walk off with the evening, y'know?

BILL

Yeah. Probably be the only rock group on the
uh... bill?

TRIPLETTE

Absolutely.

BILL

Sounds good, sounds inviting.

TRIPLETTE

Yeah. And I think you do get a lot of big audience
from these country guys.

BILL
Is this just network or is it, uh —

TRIPLETTE
No, it's better, it's really better than network. It's going to be syndicated. It'll show all over for almost a year and a half.

Mary comes out of the bedroom, combed and dressed in a dark blue kaftan. Suddenly, the colors in the room spring together as if someone had planned it. The men stand as she enters and smiles sweetly.

MARY
Here are your glasses, sweetheart.

BILL
Oh, thanks. This is John Triplette. My wife, Mary.

She and Triplette shake hands.

BILL
Why don't you sit down, dear?

She sits gracefully in his chair and he stands behind.

BILL
He's the fella from that television thing that they're doing for Hal Phillip Walker.

MARY (lights a cigarette)
Mmmm.

BILL
He's offered us a spot. (to Triplette) You're doing some great promotion for that guy.

Triplette smiles, part at the compliment, part at Mary's beauty.

Anyway, we got a great spot on this gala and we're gonna walk away with the show, John says.

She picks up a jar of face cream and begins to apply it thickly. Triplette watches as her unencumbered beauty disappears under a few swift strokes of cold cream.

MARY
We can't vote for him. We're registered Democrats. Besides, he's a little crazy, isn't he?

TRIPLETTE (laughing)
Well . . . a . . . they're all a little crazy, Mary. That's the name of the game. I think the thing you should consider is your future. I think it would give you . . .

MARY (interrupting)
But, you see, it really does make a difference be-

cause we are registered Democrats.

TRIPLETTE (laughing)

Well, I'm a registered Democrat.

Mary, her face now completely cream-covered, puffs on her cigarette.

BILL

The only reason we're registered Democrats is because your father's a registered Democrat.

Then Mary looks up at him and says finally:

MARY

Well, Tom's a registered Democrat and he wouldn't do it.

Cut.

INTERIOR, TOM'S MOTEL ROOM, DAY.

Tom sits on the bed working out some chords. His mirror is newly inscribed with "I love you," written in lipstick. The shades are pulled back and reveal smiling Norman as he knocks at the door, Tom tells him to come in and he sits down on the foot of the bed, discovering a pair of girl's underpants as he does. He stuffs them under the covers.

NORMAN

Hi, Tom.

TOM

Hi, Norman, how you doing?

NORMAN

Oh good... Sure glad you called. Is there anything I can —

TOM

You don't have any speckled birds, do you?

NORMAN

What?

TOM

L.A. turnarounds, uppers?

NORMAN

No, no — but I can get you some grass. I know where —

TOM

No thanks, I don't want any grass.

NORMAN

Okay. Uh... can I ask you a question?

TOM
Hmm?

NORMAN
Is there something... Are you angry at Bill?

TOM
No.

NORMAN
Oh... 'Cause I... I, you know, I, uh, Bill and Mary... Bill, I mean... seems to be (he sighs)... I'm just confused.

Tom hands him the guitar as he rises and goes to the phone.

TOM
Here. Write yourself a hit.

Norman picks up the instrument and runs through a series of simple chords, making them seem more difficult than they are, as Tom tries to call a girl named Cherry on the telephone.

Cut.

EXTERIOR, STREET, NIGHT.
The Walker truck drives with its P.A. going to the headquarters garage (known as the Walker-Talker-Sleeper), and goes inside. As the door slides closed, Kenny and his violin case, with his self-portrait on the lid, walk by, stop, and look up at the source of the sound.

P.A.
Does it make sense that the churches should remain untaxed on their vast holdings of land and corporate investments? Does it make sense that a multimillion-dollar income should go untaxed year after year? No, all will not be easy, but we will bask in the satisfaction of having done what we should have done— and if we don't, we may run out of tomorrows.

Cut

MONDAY, FOURTH DAY.
EXTERIOR, BUS YARD, DAY.
Looking down, we see row after row after row of parked yellow schoolbuses, waiting for summer to be over. Opal walks down one of the rows, expounding again.

>   OPAL
> The buses? The buses are empty and look menacing, threatening as so many yellow dragons. Watching me with their hollow, vacant eyes, I wonder how many little black children and little white children have yellow nightmares, their own special brand of fear for the yellow peril. No... one can't say that — damn it. I've got to be more positive. No, more negative.

She turns a corner and the Tricycle Man stands shaving at one of the bus's mirrors. His laundry is strung out on a line between two of the buses. He watches her go by, but she's too involved to notice.

>   OPAL
> Start again. Yellow is the color of caution. No. Yellow is the color of cowardice. Yellow's the color of sunshine and yet I see very little sunshine in the lives of the little black children and the little white children. I see their lives rather as a study in grayness, a mixture of black and white... of Christ, no, that's fascist. Oh, yellow, yellow, yellow **Fever**...

Cut.

INTERIOR, HOSPITAL CORRIDOR, DAY.
Delbert stands talking to Triplette on the phone at the hospital desk. Pvt. Kelly stands by the mailbox writing his mother another postcard to tell her of Barbara-Jean's health.

>   DEL
> Well, what about the place?

>   TRIPLETTE
> Not bad, not bad at all.

>   DEL
> Think it'll work out?

>   TRIPLETTE
> Yeah, they've got some sort of bizarre stage that drops out of the ceiling.

There is an oncoming wave of noise and activity at the end of the hall. Barbara-Jean is leaving with nurses, well wishes, a bouquet of flowers, her hairdresser, Jewel, and Barnett leading the pack. He seems anxious to get her out of there and back to work. We hear Barbara-Jean's voice over everything.

> DEL
> There's no getting
> there this morning.
> Wait a minute; here
> comes Barnett.

> BARBARA-JEAN
> Bye-bye, bye. I
> hope you get out
> soon, too.

As the ensemble reaches the elevator, Del signals Barnett to the phone. Mr. Green steps off the elevator with another bouquet of hand-picked flowers and bumps into Barbara-Jean

> GREEN
> How are you? You just goin' home
> BARBARA-JEAN
> I'm goin' home.

and Pvt. Kelly, who stands
beaming, close enough to
touch Barbara-Jean but just
taking her in instead.

MR. GREEN
Well, I'm glad to hear that.

BARBARA-JEAN
Thank you. How's Mrs. Green?

MR. GREEN
She's fine and she's going to be so thrilled to hear I saw
you again.

BARBARA-JEAN
Oh, good. Give her my very best. Is she takin' her
vitamin E?

MR. GREEN (patting his pocket)
Got 'em right here.

BARBARA-JEAN
All right. Good for you.

MR. GREEN
You take care.

BARBARA-JEAN
I will darlin', bye-bye.

Barnett reprimands Delbert for putting him on the phone with Triplette, and then moves in without missing a beat as Barbara-Jean sings her way onto the elevator.

BARNETT
All right, come on, come on. We gotta go with those white horseshoes, huh? We're gonna live with those for infamy. Delbert, take that cortege on the other elevator.

Which Delbert does with a sigh, leaving Pvt. Kelly at the mailbox and Mr. Green at the desk talking to the head nurse.

NURSE
I'm really sorry I have to tell you this. Mrs. Green expired this morning.

MR. GREEN(not having heard properly)
What?

NURSE
Mrs. Green died this morning.
He looks at her blankly; he heard correctly the first time.

NURSE
Wait right here. I'll get the doctor.

Mr. Green stands in shock as an enthusiastic Pvt. Kelly comes to him at the desk.

PVT. KELLY
Mr. Green, you know my momma saved her life. They used to live next door to each other. My mama's the one that put out the flames. She always loved Barbara-Jean more 'n anything; she's still keepin' a scrapbook on her. Only thing she said to me when I joined up was "Son, when you're doin' your travels, I want you to see Barbara-Jean. You don't have to say nothin' about me or nothin' like that, I just want you to see Barbara-Jean." So that's what I'm doin'. Now I'm going to go over to Opryland and hear her sing. You give my best to your wife, now.

Then he darts into the elevator as Mr. Green bows his head and sobs.

Cut.

INTERIOR, RED BARN DINNER SHOW THEATER, DAY.
Red-and-white checkered tables ring a stage. Bentwood chairs are stacked on top of the tables, and Triplette stands

laughing at Opal in a corner by the telephone. She has just turned off her machine.

OPAL
No, now wait a minute, don't laugh. I don't — let me — I have a theory about political assassination. You see, I believe that people like Madame Pearl and all these people here in this country who carry guns are the real assassins. Because they stimulate the other innocent people who eventually are the ones who pull the trigger.

INTERIOR, GREEN HOUSE, DAY.
Kenny stands in the hall talking long distance. L.A. Joan, in a tiny top and underpants, makes her way down the hall, circling around him like a skinny cat. She comes up and stops by him, he turns his back, and she moves into his bedroom.

KENNY
Ma?

MOTHER (voice-over)
Kenny, Kenny, where are you, Kenny?

KENNY
I'm in Nashville; how are you?

MOTHER (voice-over)
I've been so worried. I'm all right, haven't been able to sleep. I had to take some of that Nyquil, so I could go to sleep. It puts you right out — where are you?

KENNY
Did it help?

MOTHER (voice-over)
Yes, it did, but where are you in Nashville?

L.A. Joan circles around
him again and stops for a
question.

> KENNY
> In a rooming house.

> L.A. JOAN
> Who are you talking
> to?

MOTHER (voice-over)
. . . A rooming
house?

> KENNY
> To my mother.

MOTHER (voice-over)
Who're you talking
to, Kenny?

> KENNY
> A girl who lives in
> the rooming house.
> Her uncle owns it.

L.A. Joan goes back into
Kenny's room.

MOTHER (voice-over)
A man owns the
rooming house?
Well, it can't be very
clean.

> KENNY
> Don't be silly.

MOTHER (voice-over)
I'll bet the sheets
aren't very clean,
and you know this is
a terrible time in the
South. You can pick
up this parasite
fungus.

L.A. Joan picks up the
violin case.
Kenny sees her.

KENNY
Put — Joan — put
that down!

MOTHER (voice-over)
Kenny, listen to me
you can pick up —

KENNY (into phone)
Just a minute.

L.A. JOAN
Okay. I just wanted
to look at your
fiddle.

She puts the case down
and sits on the bed.

MOTHER (voice-over)
Kenny! You can get
this parasite — .

KENNY (into phone)
What?

MOTHER (voice-over)
. . . fungus in the
South, and it's very
difficult to get rid of.
Now when are you
comin' home?

KENNY
I don't know, a
couple of weeks.

MOTHER (voice-over)
You left your blue
suit hanging in the
closet; what are you
wearing?

KENNY
I don't need my
blue —

MOTHER (voice-over)
I would really like
you to come home
as —

> KENNY (firmly)
> Mother, now listen to
> me.

> MOTHER (voice-over)
> Kenny, don't talk to me in that tone of voice.

L. A. Joan sits watching from the bed. She doesn't see his hand disconnect the call.

> KENNY (into the blank receiver)
> I love you, too, Mama. I really do; I'll see you soon.
> Bye-Bye.

He hangs up and she smiles at him.

Cut.

EXTERIOR, OPRY BELLE, DAY.

Triplette and Delbert climb onto the replica of a riverboat stage at Opryland. They pass the Opryland dancers and make their way to Barnett, who is in combat with the stage managers as Delbert approaches him.

> BARNETT
> What do you want now?

Del slaps him on the shoulder.

> TRIPLETTE
> How you doing?

> BARNETT
> This guy wants her to do four shows today. What do you want?

> DEL
> Don't let her do too much now. How you hangin'? You feelin' better now that she's feelin' better?

> BARNETT
> Yeah, fine.

> DEL
> I gotta talk to you. We're gonna do a show, John, here...

> BARNETT
> Uh huh.

> DEL
> Haven's gonna do it. We want Barbara-Jean to head-line it.

Barbara-Jean, dressed in a pink and white pinafore with pink ribbons, comes toward them, stopping to have her picture taken, talking rather loudly about being rushed.

DEL
. . . for this candidate, Hal Phillip Walker.

BARNETT
No — absolutely not.

TRIPLETTE (interrupting)
Listen, Barnett, we don't want her to make a political statement.

BARNETT
What do you think her bein' there's gonna be?

TRIPLETTE
Well, it's —

BARNETT
ain't that gonna be a political statement?

DEL
Barnett. . .

BARNETT
No! Don't take it personal, but no, fellas. No politics, no government, no nothin'. All right?

DEL
All right.

BARNETT
Okay? I heard you out, right?

Barbara-Jean comes to them and says hello to the men, who look a little buried right now. Barnett and she sweep off, Barnett doing combat now against the members of the entourage who follow behind like sheep. Delbert turns to Triplette:

TRIPLETTE
The hell with it. We don't need her.

DEL
No, John, no. Now leave it to me. I'm gonna stay with this thing. I'm gonna follow him like a rodent, man.

Triplette laughs and onstage Barbara-Jean walks down the ramp, takes the microphone, and begins to sing.

Pvt. Kelly stands in front of the grandstand and Opal enters looking for a seat in the front row. Finally, she sits in the aisle by Pvt. Kelly and several Shriners. The grandstand is full and quiet through the next two choruses of her song.

BARBARA-JEAN

He's got a tapedeck
in his tractor
And he listens to the
local news
He finds out where
the boys are fighting
While he's plowin' to
the country blues.
He was a cowboy
And he knew I loved
him well—
A cowboy's secrets
you can never tell—
No, there's nothin'
like the lovin'
Of a hard-drivin'
cowboy man.
No, there's nothing
like the muscles of a
hard-drivin' cowboy
man.

As she comes to the end,
the applause starts and
lasts as the musicians
seque into the next song.
As she starts to sing again,
Kenny enters and stands
next to Pvt. Kelly, as there
are no seats left. He
watches Barbara-Jean
intently. Opal leans over
to Pvt. Kelly with her
microphone:

> **OPAL**
> Have you been in
> Vietnam?

PVT. KELLY (nodding to
    the music)
    Huh?

> **OPAL**
> Oh yes you have. I
> can tell by your
> face. Was it awful?

It's that careless
disrespect
I can't take no more,
baby.
It's the way that you
don't love me
When you say you
do, baby.
It hurts so bad it gets
me down, down,

PVT. KELLY (shakes his head)
It was kinda hot and wet.

OPAL
Being a trained killer, do you carry a gun?

PVT. KELLY
Just airborne is all. You think maybe I could hear Barbara-Jean sing?

OPAL
Oh, excuse me.

down.
I want to walk away from
This battleground,
This hurtin' match, it ain't no good.
I'd give a lot to love you
The way I used to do.
Wish I could . . .
Writin' it down
Kinda makes me feel better,
Kinda makes me feel better,
Keeps me away from them blues.
I wanta be nice to you, baby,
Treat you right.
The song continues to the

end. The music goes out,
the applause comes up,
and she begins to talk to
the audience, while the
musicians vamp.

BARBARA-JEAN

Last night I thanked my lucky stars that I could be here
to sing for you. And I heard on the radio the cutest little
boy.

The musicians stop vamping and she continues.

He was nine years old and you know how sometimes
the DJ'll play a tune and ask everybody to phone in
and say how they like it, you know? And, uh, I was
listening to it and, uh, they asked for callers to call in,
this little nine-year-old boy called in an' the song had
voices in the background like the way they usually
back up voices these days sometimes, you know.
Sounded like little munchkins? He called up and the
DJ said, "And how old are you, son?" An' the boy said,
"I'm nine and I think it's gonna be a hit."

She laughs.

And I thought that was so cute. Because—well I can

sing like a munchkin myself, I don't know about you, and I'm real fond of the Wizard of Oz an' plus I live out y'know just a ways out here on — offa Highway Interstate 24 on the road to Chattanooga so you can see why I kinda related to that and I — I dunno, I think me and the boys are gonna strike up another tune for you now. Let's go, boys.

She turns to the band and they begin again. Barbara-Jean looks up at the sky and puts her hand to her head.

BARBARA-JEAN

I think there's a storm a-brewing. That's what my granddaddy used to say before he lost his hearin' and sometimes he'd say, "Oh gosh," or "Durn it," or "My word."

The musicians stop again and look at one another like she's gone round the bend. Barnett lifts his glasses to his forehead and watches her. He doesn't know what to make of it. Del and Triplette watch her behind Barnett.

My granny, she'd go round the house clickin' her false teeth to the radio all day. She was a lot of fun and always cooked my favorite roast beef and she was a sweetheart. She raised chickens, too. She, uh — in fact, did ya ever hear a chicken sound? You know how chickens go?

She makes a chicken sound.

Here chick, chick, chick, chick, chick, chick, here chick, chick, chick. Well, anyway I guess we better strike up this tune before it's too late. Okay, boys —

The music comes in. She starts to talk again.

I'm thinkin', y'know, about the — first job I ever really got was when Mama —

The music stops.

. . . my grandma, she, she's the one who clacked her false teeth to the radio all day? She taught my mama how to sing an' mama taught me. One time she took me down 'cause we was gonna get a new Frigidaire, an' she took me down to the Frigidaire store where the man was doin' the advertisin', this little record was goin' round and round an' my mama told him that I knew how to sing.

The audience begins to react, as do Barnett, the band, Triplette, and Delbert.

He said if she can learn this tune and comes down and sings it to me, I'll give y'all a quarter. So Mama and I went home and then what happened — let's see, I think — oh, yeah — we went home and I learned both sides of the record in half an hour and we went back there and pranced in real fancy and I told 'im that I'd learned 'em and he said, well, let me hear this, so I sang 'im both sides of the record instead of just one, so he gave us fifty cents and we went across the street and had us a soda.

She laughs.

Ever since then I been workin', I don't—I think ever since then I been workin' and doin' my...

At this point, Barnett, deeply concerned, starts down the ramp with two of the dancers to get her. Triplette and Delbert keep watching on stage as Barbara-Jean continues, lost in her mind somewhere.

BARNETT

Come on, boys, come on.

BARBARA-JEAN

... supportin' myself — anyway

BARNETT (kindly)

Hey, hey!

She looks at him and cowers slightly, then looks away from him.

BARBARA-JEAN

Am I all right?

BARNETT

Gonna get you some lemonade, darlin'...You're fine, darlin', fine. It's the microphone. Gimme the mike —

BARBARA-JEAN

I ain't done.

BARNETT

I know, I know.

BARBARA-JEAN

I ain't done.

BARNETT (gently)

Go get a glass of water. Boys, help her off, all right? You'll come back, okay, darlin', come on.

The boys come forward and start her up the ramp and off-stage. She turns and waves to the audience, but the reaction is grim. They catcall, and boo, some even throw things out

onto the stage. Pvt. Kelly, heartbroken, shouts to the audience to be still, but to no avail. Barnett talks to the disappointed crowd.

BARNETT
Aw, come on now, have a heart now.

He is interrupted by a holocaust of boos, which continue as he speaks.

BARNETT
You don't mean that, do you?

The orchestra starts to play, but Barnett tells them to stop.

> That little girl just came out of the hospital — did you know that? That little girl's in there cryin' her eyes out 'cause she didn't want to disappoint you.

The sounds against her are more than he can bear. He looks around him and panics, not wanting to cause a breach between the fans and his fragile wife. He makes a desperate move to pacify them.

BARNETT (abruptly)
You all show up at Centennial Park tomorrow at the Parthenon — you'll see her for free as our guest. How's that, huh?

The boos continue, but the cheers and applause that filter in lead him to believe that it was the right thing to do.

> All right, let's hear a welcome — a get-well welcome for Barbara-Jean.

And as the boos change to applause, Barnett makes his way up the ramp to Delbert and Triplette, who stand concerned.

BARNETT
Ingrates is all they are... ingrates... and you guys know it. They got me trapped out there.

TRIPLETTE
I know you did, Barnett.

BARNETT
I want some ground rules.

TRIPLETTE (sincerely)
You name it.

BARNETT (perspiring heavily)
She's gonna sing first, right?

TRIPLETTE
Right.

BARNETT

She's gonna be off before that man of yours even shows.

BARNETT

I never should have
brought her here in
the first place.

TRIPLETTE

Fine. Whatever you
want, Barnett.

BARNETT

No paraphernalia, no literature being circulated, you understand?

TRIPLETTE

Right.

BARNETT

And never in any way or shape or form is she to be associated with Hal Phillip Walker...whatever his name is—

Cut.

INTERIOR, REESE HOME, DAY.
Linnea sits talking on the phone.

LINNEA

Hello.

TOM (voice-over)
Hey, guess who...Linnea?

LINNEA

Yes, it's me.

TOM (voice-over)
Hi. This is me. Listen, I'm playing a gig tonight, down-town; you wanta come and meet me?

Linnea seems unable to answer.

TOM (voice-over)
It's called the...uh...No Exit or the Exit Out, some-thing like that. Anyway, it's right across the street from Friday's on Church. You know where that is, don't you? Anyhow, I'll be there at eight and...uh, why don't you meet me there? Okay?

LINNEA

Ummmm...

Before she can make up an excuse, he hangs up, leaving her

caught up in the cross-current of her fifteen-year marriage and how to cope with her body which has just come to life.

Cut.

The Exit Inn is an intimate home away from home for musicians and their friends, who come out of the audience to perform as often as from the stage. Norman, Bill, Mary and Opal sit at a table near the stage drinking champagne, as gravel-voiced Johnny Barnett performs.

> **JOHNNY** (sings)
> Well, it's sad but true.
> The pilot light of our love
> Has flickered out. . .

> **OPAL**
> Driver — Driver, could I have a wee bit more champagne?

Bill leans over and whispers to her —

> **BILL**
> His name is Norman.

> **OPAL**
> Norman, oh yes, Norman. . .

He pours her glass full.

> **OPAL**
> Oh, thank you so much, Norman.

> **JOHNNY** (singing)
> Since my baby's cookin'
> In another man's pan.

Linnea enters the room from the other side. She stands in the corner trying to adjust to the light and sees Tom. She spots him in a direction away from Bill and Mary. She works her way through the crowd to Tom, but from yet another direction L. A. Joan, in black wig and gypsy skirt, darts in and sits down next to him. Linnea turns, goes to the back of the room, and sits down in a wooden booth. Wade sits nearby and talks to the waitress who turns to take her order.

> **LINNEA**
> I'll have a cider.

> **WAITRESS**
> Cider?

> **WADE** (leaning in)
> Put it on my bill.

LINNEA
Oh, no—

WADE
Yes.

LINNEA
All right, would you put it in a wineglass for me?

WADE (to waitress)
Put it in a wineglass and put it on my bill.

Wade gets up beer in hand and moves to Linnea's booth. He sits down beside her.

L.A. JOAN
Hi...

TOM
Hi...

L.A. JOAN
You know what it says on the ladies-room mirror?

TOM
No.

L.A. JOAN
It said, "I'm stuck here at the exit and with no place left to go."

WADE
My name's Wade Coolidge. What's yours?

LINNEA (not quite knowing what to do)
Oh, my... ah... Linnea's my name.

Across the room Opal holds forth.

OPAL
Traveling in cozy quarters, I mean you sort of have to camp in one room.

OPAL
Obviously, yes.

BILL.
Well, Mary and I camp in one room and Tom camps in a lotta rooms.

JOHNNY (singing)
Well, if makin' love was margarine, then she is the high-priced spread.

OPAL
Actually, I shouldn't ask you this, Mary... well, he is so attractive. Shall we say that Tom and I were...

Opal giggles inanely and says "La-de-da", as Mary turns away from her rude behavior and watches the stage. Bill pursues, wanting to find out where Tom is.

                              BILL
          You sang together.

                             OPAL
          Oh no, . . . I mean . . . we sort of got to know each other
          in the Biblical sense, if you know what I mean . . .

                              BILL
          You went to bed with him, right?
Mary continues to look at the stage as Bill drives on.

                             OPAL
          Oh yes, I thought you understood that.

                              BILL
          Uh huh. Where did you go to bed with him?
The vocalist onstage has finished, and through the applause
he anounces that his friend Tom Frank is in the audience and
has agreed to do a couple of numbers. Bill and Mary look
amazed and Opal is thrilled.

                             OPAL
          Speak of the devil!

                              BILL
          Well, I'll be damned!
Tom makes his way to the stage as the audience continues to
clap. Wade, in his enthusiasm, splashes a little beer on Linnea
who tries to brush it off casually.

                        TOM (from stage)
          Thank you. Uh . . . you may remember I used to be
          part of a trio . . .

                        BILL (from table)
          Used to be?

                              TOM
          I've been hiding from them all week, but it seems
          they found me here tonight, so we might as well have
          them up here, too.
Opal leads the applause and pats Mary enthusiastically.·

                             OPAL
          Oh, you must.
As they get up and make their way to the stage, the audience
breaks into a ragged version of "It Don't Worry Me." Tom nods
at Bill, and Mary's eyes bore through him. They take their
positions and begin "Since You've Gone," with Mary playing
most of the song to Tom. Wade talks to Linnea.

WADE
All I need is fifteen
minutes a night.

LINNEA
Fifteen minutes?

WADE
Sleep. That's all I
need. Don't want to
waste no time
sleeping.

LINNEA
Oh.
Wade hums with them for
a moment and Linnea
buries a smile.

WADE
I was in prison for
twenty-eight
years. . . . You
married?

TRIO (singing)
Since you've gone
my heart is broken
Another time.

MARY (sings)
Oh, railroad train is
taking him from me.
All my luxury has
turned to misery.
He's all I ever
wanted.
Why did he run from
me?
Since you've gone,
my heart is broken
Another time.

TRIO (sings)
Since you've gone
my heart is broken
Another time.

LINNEA
Uh . . . uh, yes I am.
Across the way Opal has
stuck her microphone in a
candle. Norman leans in.

NORMAN
Listen, when this is
over I'll be taking
them back and after
that we could ride
around and I could
tell you things that
would send you
around the corner.

OPAL (interrupting)
Uh . . . oh, what is
your name?

NORMAN
Norman.

MARY (sings)
I didn't know that
you were leaving
Till you were out the
door.
I didn't know the
love you gave
Was a real love.
I didn't know a lot of
things then
Lord, I know them
now.

OPAL	TRIO (sings)
Norman. Please, Norman, I make it a point never to gossip with servants.	Since you've gone, my heart is broken Another time. Since you've gone my heart is broken Another time.

Cut.

INTERIOR, RED BARN DINNER THEATER, NIGHT.

Delbert stands in his biege plaid suit and white shoes inside the ring of red-and-white-checkered tables talking to an all-male audience. Behind the highest level of tables, we see Albequerque hiding behind a red velvet curtain. Outside she saw a sign that said "Benefit" and figuring it was her's, she entered through the kitchen and now stands eating some of the leftovers.

DELBERT

Okay, fellas, I think you know we got a good man to get behind here, and I don't want to take a whole lotta your time because we have some entertainment for you. You got pledge cards on the table. Pledge anything you want to and I'll be sure and make you pay it. You got a check in your pocket, don't be afraid to write it out. I'll get it to the banks quick before you can stop it. Cash, anything, don't be humble or shy, and so you won't get bored there's something coming to keep you occupied.

And as he tells them to keep their eyes up, a stage slowly descends from the ceiling carrying a playing band and Sueleen Gay, dressed in green complete with mask, hood and green beauty mark. Whistles and applause greet her entrance.

SUELEEN

Hi y'all—I'm Sueleen Gay and I'm here to sing you a song about a girl who never gets enough...

The men "ooh," and after too many vamps, she slips into the song, literally, about a tone and a half under pitch. She dances around the stage for a full chorus of "I Never Get Enough of the Love I'm Hungry For." Triplette leans into Delbert, who sits next to a drunk Bud Hamilton, and says:

> TRIPLETTE
Worst singer I ever heard.

> DEL (laughing)
She cannot sing a lick, can she?

Bud wads up some dollar bills and starts to throw them at the stage, but Sueleen continues with:

> I ain't greedy for that mansion on the hill,
> I never was that blind,
> Don't need my pockets stuffed
> With hundred-dollar bills...

Cut.

INTERIOR, NO EXIT INN, NIGHT.

Bill and Mary having finished their song, make their way back to the table through the applause. Wade pounds his beer on the table in approval, and as Tom tosses Mary her jacket from the stage, Wade excuses himself to Linnea and heads for the Men's room.

> TOM
All right, if you want more it's gonna have to be me alone, 'cause I just been deserted.

He sits down.

> I'm gonna play something I wrote recently and came down here to record. I'm going to dedicate this to someone kind of special who just might be here tonight. It's called "I'm Easy."

He begins to play the introduction as Opal looks down shyly and smiles, sure that he intends it for her. Mary shifts in her seat and L.A. Joan from her part of the room sits and smiles. His focus goes into the audience and, now all alone in the booth, Linnea watches him.

A particular kind of quiet takes over in the room, and Tom caresses the notes as he sings. For a while, each of the younger women in Tom's life takes the song in as being meant for her. But about midway through, Mary detects another stakeout. She looks back, which causes Opal to

> TOM (singing)
It's not my way to love you
Just when no one's looking.
It's not my way to take your hand
If I'm not sure.
It's not my way to let you see
What's going on inside of me

peer around looking for the receiver. L.A. Joan looks around, saddened by his lack of interest, and as he continues the song, it becomes a quiet dialogue between he and Linnea, who now sits motionless, her eyes soft with tears.

When it's a love you
won't be needing
If you're not free.
Please stop pullin' at
my sleeve
If you're just playing,
If you won't take the
things
You make me want
to give.
I never cared too
much for games
And this one is
driving me insane.
You're not half as
free
To wander as you
claim.
Because I'm easy,
yeah, I'm easy.
Give the word and
I'll play the game
As though that's how
it ought to be
Because I'm easy...
Cut.

INTERIOR, RED BARN DINNER THEATRE, NIGHT.
The applause is loud for Sueleen, no doubt because she has stopped singing. Unfortunately, this encourages her and she moves into the next song quickly. As she does, she removes her cape. There are a few cheers hoping that she is getting on with the business at hand. Instead, she continues singing the too-slow tempo, no-pitch rendition of "One, I Love You." The men are no longer polite and begin to boo and throw things onto the stage. She sticks it out for what seems an inordinately long time. Triplette, who's afraid they will lose pledges, turns to Delbert, who answers his look.

DELBERT
Did you tell Trout exactly what you wanted?

TRIPLETTE (bristling and passing the buck)
Did I tell Trout? It was your job, Del.

DEL (shaking his head)
Well, I didn't think there was going to be...
At this point, Sueleen tearfully puts the microphone down on the piano and runs up the stairs toward the curtains where Albequerque continues to stand and eat unseen. Delbert comes to Sueleen. The men have started to clap in time and shout for her to "take it all off."

DEL
What's the matter, honey?

SUELEEN
I don't know what's goin' on here.

DEL
Now listen, didn't Trout tell you you're supposed to strip?
Sueleen ignores the possibility that a striptease was ever intended.

SUELEEN
I'm a singer.
Triplette's eyes roll back in his head. Then, he reaches over and grabs her by the arm and lies to her sincerely.

TRIPLETTE

Listen — you go on down and finish the show like you
told Trout you would and I'll set it up so you can sing at
the Parthenon.

SUELEEN (tempted)

I get to sing at the Parthenon with Barbara-Jean?

TRIPLETTE

Yes, now go on down and finish...

SUELEEN (defensively)

Someday I'm gonna be a bigger star than Barbara-
Jean.

TRIPLETTE

Aw, I know you are. You can't miss.

DELBERT

These fellows really like you, honey.

She walks down the stairs accompanied by cheers and applause. For the first time, she determines it wasn't her singing
they liked at all. The band goes into some basic "take-it-off"
music and she starts with the gloves and tosses them to the
audience. Not knowing exactly what to do next, she undoes

the top of her gown which falls to her waist revealing her peach-colored brassiere, and suddenly she knows that she isn't in a dream, that St. Theresa won't save her and that in order to survive she must proceed. From the bra she pulls out first one sweat sock and then the other. Both go out into the surprised audience. Angry and scared, she slips the dress to the floor and, half stumbling, tosses it to the eager crowd of men, who couldn't like her more if they tried. Next comes the bra itself, revealing very innocent breasts. As she continues to circle the stage, a slim piano fanfare begins. She doffs her yellow nylon panties and walks naked up the stairs to a cheering, standing ovation. Albequerque, who is overjoyed by the unexpected performance, stands outside the curtains clapping as Sueleen passes by her numbly, her dignity left out there in the middle of the floor somewhere.

CUT.

INTERIOR, TOM'S MOTEL ROOM, NIGHT.
Once again, we see the turning spools on the tape deck and hear Tom's voice singing:

> **TOM** (singing on tape)
> Take my hand and pull me down.
> I won't put up any fight
> Because I'm easy.

In bed, Tom lights a cigarette and Linnea watches him for a moment quietly.

> **LINNEA**
> You want to learn how to say something in sign language?

He turns and smiles at her.

> **TOM**
> Yeah. How do you say I love you?

LINNEA (demonstrating)
Well, you could say — well you could say it in shorthand. This is shorthand.
He imitates her gesture and they look at one another.

TOM (on tape singing)
Love you from a distance
When your eyes throw light at mine
Say you want me, I'll come running.

LINNEA

Or you could say I love you...

TOM (repeating)

I love you.

LINNEA

Mmm, or you could just say — I'm happy I met you...

TOM

I'm happy I met you.

They look at one another again as he imitates the gesture,
then she waves the smoke away from his cigarette.

LINNEA

Phew! How can you smoke those things?

TOM

Oh.

LINNEA

Let me have a drag.

TOM

Do you smoke?

LINNEA

No.

TOM

What do you want to do that for?

She takes a puff of the cigarette and exhales the smoke like a
woman in a "bad woman" movie. He takes the cigarette
away from her and kisses her on the cheek.

LINNEA

No?

TOM

Mmm.

LINNEA

So what?

She smiles and they look at each other again, then she
reaches over, picking up her watch from the bedside table.
The tape deck stops and begins to rewind.

LINNEA

I have to go.

                          TOM
        Oh — can't you just call them or something?

                        LINNEA

                   No, no I can't.
She puts on her watch, gets out of bed but doesn't move for a
moment as Tom runs his hand down her slip-covered back.

                          TOM
                Can't you stay another hour?

                        LINNEA

                   No, no...
Then gently with her back to him still.
        I just can't.
She rises and makes her way to the closet where her clothes
are hung. He watches her for a moment. She's touched him,
but he decides on his usual way out and picks up the phone.
Linnea begins to dress and continues to do so as he makes his
long-distance telephone connection.

                  GIRL (voice-over)

        Hello?

                          TOM

        Hey —

                  GIRL (voice-over)

        Oh, wow!... I...
Tom interrupts, telling her he's sorry he left the way he did, but
because the girl has lived with him through thick and thin,
mostly thin, she steers the conversation away from recrimina-
tion. Linnea washes in the basin.

                          TOM
             Listen, can you come down here?

                  GIRL (voice-over)

        When?

                          TOM

        Tonight.

                  GIRL (voice-over)

        Oh Tom, I can't do that.
They discuss her job, his wanting her to quit her job, her
reasons for not wanting to, as Linnea searches under the
covers for and finds her underpants tangled on Tom's foot.

She smiles at him and puts them in her purse. Then she walks to Tom, who leans forward to her, shielding the mouthpiece for a moment, and they kiss.

Linnea moves to the door with no regrets, having taken the best Tom has to offer. She turns before she leaves, and makes the "I'm happy I met you" sign. He signs back.

GIRL (voice-over)
When are you coming home?

TOM
'Bout a week.

LINNEA
Bye.

Girl (voice-over)
I miss you.

GIRL (voice-over)
New York's missed you, too. Weather's been terrific.

TOM
Yeah?

Linnea closes the door behind her.

GIRL (voice-over)
What's that?

TOM (lying)
Just room service . . . uh, there's fifty cents on the desk there, just pick it up.

GIRL (laughing)
Big tipper.

The walls seem to push in a little on Tom.

TOM
Well, times are hard you know.

GIRL (voice-over)
All that money. You can really afford to bring me down, I see.

TOM (suddenly impatient)
Well, never mind. I'll see you in a week.

GIRL (voice-over)
I love you, Tom.

He hangs up abruptly and contemplates his first night in Nashville alone and his basic fear of falling asleep and never waking up.

EXTERIOR, SUELEEN'S APARTMENT, NIGHT

Wade walks downstairs to his room in the basement of the Bell
apartment-hotel, across the street from the bus station,
Sueleen lives on the second floor. Delbert's yellow Cadillac
pulls up in front.

DEL
This it, honey? Just be careful getting out.

Sueleen, in a raincoat, gets out of his car, dragging her green
dress on the ground behind her. She enters the lobby to
collect her key at the desk, comes back out and without a
word starts up the stairs to her door. Delbert jumps out of the
front seat and places his half-finished drink on top of his car.

DELBERT
Hey! Hey, wait just a minute.

She runs up the stairs but so does he, and he grabs her arm,
stopping her at the door.

DEL
Just hold it, will ya? Now—

He moves close to her and she stiffens. Somehow, one gets
the feeling that she is still a virgin and he is still a gentleman.

DEL
Now, I know you don't do that all the time, and I. . . I'm
gonna tell you that I just mean—me personally, boy
I—you know I'd just like to—I'd like to kiss you every
place, you know what I'm telling you? I think you. . .

Wade sticks his head around the stairwell and starts up.

WADE
Sueleen? You okay?

Delbert drops her arm and starts down the stairs quickly like a
child caught at the cookie jar.

DEL
Shit, man. . . .

Wade continues up the stairs as Sueleen studies them both in
silence. Delbert gets into his car and as he drives off we hear:

DEL
Didn't your mama teach you no manners!

WADE
Who was that?

Sueleen doesn't answer.

WADE

What's the matter with you? Ain't you gonna talk to me?

She looks down at the ground.

Did it go all right?

SUELEEN

Oh, Wade.

WADE

What?

SUELEEN

I had to do me a striptease in front of all those men in order to get to sing at the Parthenon with Barbara-Jean.

WADE (Shocked)

Aw, shit, Sueleen — that's dreadful, that's terrible, girl! I mean — look — I don't know how to tell you this but I been tryin', I been meanin' to tell you this for a long time. You — you can't sing. Sueleen, you may as well face the fact that you cannot sing; you ain't never gonna be no star; I mean, I wish you'd give it up now. I mean, they gonna kill you; they gonna tear your heart out if you keep on. They gonna walk on your soul, girl!

SUELEEN (defensively)

I don't know what you're talkin' about.

WADE

But you can't sing, do you understand that?

She laughs. If anything has happened as a result of tonight, it is her determination that she has not shucked down in vain.

SUELEEN

Yeah? You wanta make a bet? You wanna just come to the Parthenon and watch me sing with Barbara-Jean?

WADE

Listen, I am leavin' for Detroit Wednesday.

She turns and opens her door.

SUELEEN

You just come an' watch me.

WADE

Listen, I am leaving for Detroit on Wednesday and if you wanna go you just come on. They gonna kill you in this town, girl!

SUELEEN
Yeah, well you come an' see.

WADE
They gonna use you, you know that.

SUELEEN
Bye, Wade.

She turns and walks inside. Wade starts down the stairs shaking his head.

WADE
Shit. Don't know why I stick around when she makes me so goddam mad I could spit.

Cut.

EXTERIOR, SKY, NIGHT.
Flashing across the sky, we see "New Roots for the Nation — Hal Phillip Walker" appear, one letter at a time, on a news blimp. We hear Howard K. Smith in the background.

HOWARD K. SMITH
Little more than a year ago, a man named Hal Phillip Walker excited a group of college students with some questions. Have you stood on a high and windy hill and heard the acorns drop and roll? Have you walked in the valley beside the brook, walked alone and remembered —

Dissolve.

TUESDAY, FIFTH DAY.
CLOSE-UP, HOWARD K. SMITH, DAY.
On television we see Howard K. Smith, as a woman and her family sit in the foreground, waiting for the festivities to begin at the Parthenon in Centennial Park.

HOWARD K. SMITH
Does Christmas smell like oranges to you? Well, in the commencement speech such questions were fitting perhaps, but hardly the material with which to launch a presidential campaign.

EXTERIOR, PARTHENON, CENTENNIAL PARK, DAY.
Now we see a large stage platform in front of a huge American flag. Under the flag, a long Hal Phillip Walker banner and

Hal Phillip Walker is in a way a mystery man. Out of nowhere, with a handful of students and scarcely any professionals, he's

a podium with a "New Roots for the Nation" poster on it. The large tents along the side provide food and drink and shelter for the hundreds of fans, who are starting to make their way to the park. Sound and equipment men crawl over the stage and lawn, setting up apparatus, as the Walker truck pulls up and parks next to Tommy Brown's large van. In back of all this stands the Parthenon itself. At either end of it are machines whereby, for a quarter, one can hear a complete dramatization of how they came to build it in the first place, affording Nashville with the title, "The Athens of the South."

managed to win three presidential primaries and is given a fighting chance to take a fourth—Tennessee. A win in that state would take on added significance, for only once in the last fifty years has Tennessee failed to vote for a winning presidential candidate. No doubt, many Americans, especially party-liners, wish that Hal Phillip Walker would go away, disappear like the natural frost and come again at some more convenient season. But whatever he may be doing, it seems sure that Hal Phillip Walker is not going away. For there is genuine appeal and it...

HOWARD K. SMITH

...may be related to the raw courage of this man running for president—willing to battle vast oil companies, eliminate subsidies to farmers, tax churches, abolish the electoral college, change the national anthem, and remove lawyers from government, especially from Congress. Well, at this point it would be wise to say most of us don't know the answer to Hal Phillip Walker. But to answer one of his questions: as a matter of fact, Christmas has always smelled like oranges to me.

HAL PHILLIP WALKER

new roots for the nation

REPLACEMENT PARTY
PRESIDENT

On the back side of the Parthenon, we see an official-looking cavalcade of black limousines, police cars and motorcycles enter the park with their lights on. One of them has small American flags on the fenders. The Tricycle Man drives into the park past Opal and a throng of people hurrying to get a place. On the other side of the park we hear Wade in his truck, yelling to the oncoming traffic that they're going the wrong way. In the background, we hear this song —

SONG
Our country cries for peace today.

There's trouble in the U. S. A.
Watergate is the sound that rings.
Wonder what this year will bring.
Wonder what this year will bring.
Or will the sun refuse to shine?
Wonder what this year will bring...
Down in Nashville I heard today,
Shortage of food is on the way. While up in Denver gas
shortage rings.
There's trouble in the U. S. A.

The cavalcade pulls up and stops behind the Parthenon, their
lights continue to flash and Triplette gets out of the car with
flags on the fenders and talks to its other occupant, Hal Phillip
Walker, whom we cannot see.

TRIPLETTE

You may have to sit out here for an hour or so; I hope
not —

WALKER (voice-over)

That's all right, John; it'll give me time to work on my
speech.

TRIPLETTE

Okay, thank you —

Triplette shakes hands with several police and plainclothes-
men who stand beside the car. Then he spots Delbert coming
across the lawn.

DEL

Hey, John, how are you?

TRIPLETTE

How are you?

DEL

A... can I say hello to —

TRIPLETTE

He's working on his speech. Come on, I want to get
this going. We'll do that later. Is Barnett here?

They climb the high steps of the Parthenon, looking like two
sandy ants approaching a hill for just a moment, and then
disappear behind the columns. When they reappear near
the busy stage, Delbert is telling the building's history.

DEL

This was originally made of lumber and plaster of Paris.
They built it for the Centennial Celebration in 1876
and the people liked it so much they didn't want it torn
down. Then Nashville got to be called "Athens of the
South" (Triplette laughs). People sort of took to that.
Then they rebuilt it . . .

TRIPLETTE

This building?

DEL

Right before I was born.

They have reached the platform and Barnett, in his usual
attire, greets them, perspiring.

BARNETT

Whoo! It's gonna be a scorcher.

TRIPLETTE (to Delbert)

Will the park police control all this?

DEL

Right.

BARNETT

Delbert, hey, Delbert get over here. Come on, we
don't need all these chairs, do we? This ain't no band
here.

By now the red-white-and-blue buntinged platform has filled
with Chamber of Commerce people, media people and
photographers. Suddenly, Barnett stops dead in his tracks. He
has seen the Walker banner and is stunned.

DEL

What's the matter, man?

BARNETT

I don't — I don't believe it!

DEL

What's the matter?

Barnett points to the banner and begins to shout.

BARNETT

Are you guys jerkin' me around? Do you see what I see
or not?

DEL
What are you talking about?

Barnett moves to Triplette.

BARNETT
What the hell is that sign doin' up there, Triplette, huh?
Now, come on we had some ground rules, am I right?
No political signs, no advertising, no nothin' — What
the hell are you doin'?

A photographer comes in and snaps a picture, as Triplette tries
to pacify him with "We'll take care of it." Barnett knows better.
He pushes the photographer aside roughly.

BARNETT
Go about your business! Now come on, lemme hear
it —

TRIPLETTE
I have abided...

BARNETT (irate)
I laid down some ground rules...

TRIPLETTE (loses his temper)
I have a man running for the presidency of this country

sitting out there in his car like a fool because of your ground rules.

BARNETT

He can sit out in the sun and parch for all I care! My wife ain't well, is she? And I brought her out of the hospital bed to be here. And you gave me some ground rules. Well, you're full of it just like your, your man!

Triplette loses control.

TRIPLETTE

I have abided by every ground rule that you laid down!

BARNETT

Except one. What is that thing up there, huh? What is that? She ain't gonna appear here with that sign up!

TRIPLETTE

I have busted my ass for you this last week, Barnett.

BARNETT

Well, I'm gonna bust your ass, too—

TRIPLETTE

And I'm through with it! Now you can take your wife and you can take a walk. . .

                    BARNETT

I'll give you a . . .

                    TRIPLETTE

And I'll get on that microphone and I'll tell these
people that she's not going to appear.

        TRIPLETTE   BARNETT
That's right!   You will huh? Well, go on
                                and do it!

                    TRIPLETTE

Take a walk and I'll do it!

                    BARNETT

You'd do that, huh?

                    TRIPLETTE

I'll do it!

                    BARNETT

You'd put a knife in my wife's back like that, man?

                    TRIPLETTE

You're putting the knife in her back, buster! You're
doing it! Now I have not got time to take the goddam
sign down and put it back up.

Barnett pulls in and reverses rationales.

                    BARNETT

What the hell are you hollerin' about in front of all
these people, huh? You trying to embarrass me?

And Triplette regains control of the issue —

                    TRIPLETTE (quietly)

I'm trying to be heard. Just trying to be heard.

As Barnett discusses moving the chairs off the stage, one
wonders how many times in how many situations he has
reversed original issues, or if this is the first time. Triplette tells
him not to worry, as Barnett turns to find Delbert.

                    BARNETT

Where is that rat? What're you hiding back there for,
you little rat, huh?

                                                    Cut.

EXTERIOR, CEMETERY, DAY.

Atop a very green, tree-covered hilltop, a small group of
people sit at graveside listening to Esther Green's eulogy. A
mist has gathered around them and they seem cut off from
the rest of the world.

MINISTER
. . . and grant us all to serve thee by day that we may
find eternal fellowship with them through Him who
died and rose again for us all, Jesus Christ, our Lord,
Amen.

Kenny is there. Last night, before he went to bed, he made
Mr. Green supper and brought it to him on a tray in bed. L. A.
Joan didn't come home, so she isn't at the funeral. Suddenly,
Green stands and starts down the hill. Kenny gets up and tries
to stop him.

KENNY
Mr. Green, where
are you going?

GREEN
To find Martha.

KENNY
What for?

GREEN
She needs to show
some respect to
Esther!

MINISTER
Our help is in the
name of the Lord. In
heaven and on
earth. . .

Mr. Green breaks from Kenny's grasp and continues down the
hill. Kenny follows him.

Cut.

EXTERIOR, PARTHENON, CENTENNIAL PARK, DAY.
For just a moment the huge American flag fills the screen
and we hear the announcer.

VOICE
Now, ladies and gentlemen, Barbara-Jean and
Haven Hamilton!

HAVEN and BARBARA-JEAN (alternately)

There are cheers and
applause as they break
into song. Haven's white
rhinestone-on-white
tailored Western suit
stands out against the

HAVEN
When I feel my life
perishing,
I call you on the
phone.

American flag, as does
Barbara-Jean's demure
white organdy pinafore.
She is, in fact, radiant,
doing what she does
best — safe for as long as
the song lasts from any of
the conflict that plagues
her, supported by her
friend, Haven, who shares
her ability to awaken
people's hopes and
dreams, allowing them to
bask for those same few
minutes in optimism. In
the audience, the Tricycle
Man moves down to the
platform and people look
at him curiously. Star
pushes his way through
the crowd in another
direction, still in pursuit of

BARBARA-JEAN
I always fix you up
When you get
broken.

HAVEN
'Cause every time
that I got hurt
And went out of
control,

BARBARA-JEAN
I knew the fears you
felt
Before you spoke
them.

TOGETHER
You tell me, one, I
love you,
Two, I'm thinking of
you,
Three, I'll never let
you go.

Albequerque, who sits
curled up on the edge of
the platform unnoticed.
Behind her stands Linnea,
whose legs feel a little
weak this morning, at her
place in the choir. Further
back stand Tom and
Mary, who can't find Bill.
Sueleen Gay, dressed in
pink satin, Martha
Washington-style, stands
firmly against one of the
pillars, mouthing the
words as Barbara-Jean
sings. Wade makes his
way through the
audience as does Opal,
craning her neck and still
trying to find the truth.
Pvt. Glen Kelly stands
front and center to the

And four, I miss you,
Five, I want to kiss
you,
six, I won't leave you
no more.

BARBARA-JEAN
When I feel my life
vanishing
like waves upon the
sand,

    HAVEN
With nothing to
replace it
But invention,

BARBARA-JEAN
So I make my
rhymes and sing my
songs,
An' still they don't
understand.

platform. L.A. Joan, now in a platinum wig and turban, holds Bill's hand and leads him through the crowd.

HAVEN

To make 'em laugh was never your intention.

TOGETHER

One, I love you,
Two, I'm thinking of you,
Three, I'll never let you go;
And four, I miss you,
Five, I want to kiss you,
Six, I won't leave you no more.
One, I love you,
Two, I'm thinking of you,
Three, I'll never let you go.
And four, I miss you,
Five, I want to kiss you,
Six, I won't leave you no more:
Six, I won't leave you no more.
Six, I won't leave you no more.

Mr. Green has arrived with Kenny who is pessimistic about finding L.A. Joan in the crowd. But Green, having had a belly full of Martha's disrespect, strikes out alone. Kenny gives up and with his ever-present violin case walks through the applauding audience. On stage, Haven kisses Barbara-Jean's hand and the band segues into the next song.

Bud and Lady Pearl stand onstage busily putting several bunches of white carnations together to give to Barbara-Jean. Tommy Brown and his wife stand between

Barbara-Jean

Thank you, thank you very much...
Mama and Daddy raised me
With love and care,
They sacrificed so

members of the Chamber of Commerce and Triplette who makes some sort of remark that they both laugh at. Delbert is there, but has swallowed himself up in the city fathers to avoid confrontation with anyone on any level, especially Barnett who stands behind the platform looking out into the audience of ingrates who picked up on his free invitation. Kenny stands watching Barbara-Jean as intently as he did at the Opry, and reaches for a key he wears around his neck as Pvt. Kelly shifts his duffel bag from one hand to the other. Opal, having run out of film, has found a television truck and is inside putting a new roll of film in the camera and chatting it up with the boys. Kenny hurriedly opens the violin case and takes something out. For a moment he watches the huge flag billow softly behind Barbara-Jean who drops a tone in color due to a passing cloud.

I could have a better share.
They fed me and clothed me,
And sent me to school
Mama taught me how to sing,
Daddy lived the golden rule.
When I think of the children
Alone and afraid, abandoned and wild,
Like a fatherless child,
I think of my mama
And how she could sing
Harmony with Daddy.
Our laughter would ring
Down the highways, on the beaches,
Just as far as mem'ry reaches.
I still hear daddy singing
His old army songs.
We'd laugh and count horses
As we drove along.
We were young then,
We were together.
We could bear floods and fire
And bad weather.

And now that I'm
older,
Grown up on my
own,
I still love Mama and
Daddy best
And my Idaho
home.
Mama grew up on
the prairies of
Kansas.
She was tender and
sweet.
The dust and
tornadoes blew
round her,
But they left her
straight up
On her feet.
My daddy grew up
on his own,
More or less, his
mama died when
He was just eleven.
He had seven sisters
to raise him,
But he dreamed of
his mama in
heaven.
His daddy drank
whiskey and had a
sharp eye,
He sold chicken
medicine
The farmers would
buy.
Together they
hunted
The fields and the
farms,
When his daddy
died,

My daddy rested
In my mama's arms,
Down the highways,
on the beaches,
Just as far as mem'ry
reaches,
I still hear Daddy
singing
His old army songs,
We'd laugh and
count horses
As we drove along.
We were young
then,
We were together.
We could bear
floods and fire
And bad weather.
And now that I'm
older,
Grown up on my
own,
I still love Mama and
Daddy best
And my Idaho
home.

As the sun comes out again, she closes her eyes and is lost in her own reveries, not seeing Pvt. Kelly, who stands mesmerized. Or Kenny, who can't take his eyes off the stage. Or the rest of the audience, who break into deafening applause as she says:

BARBARA-JEAN

For Mama and Daddy. Thank you. Thank you so much, ladies and gentlemen. Thank you.

Haven walks out onstage, arms raised. The carnations are in one hand and he takes hold of Barbara-Jean with the other. They make a wide sweeping bow, as people on stage and in the audience express their love for her the only way they can. Then she drops, like a beautiful bird shot in midflight. Haven falls too, punctuated by two sharp cracks that cut through the sound of the applause, making it seem arbitrary. In the moment when everyone must try and comprehend what has happened, Pvt. Kelly has turned, seen the source of the gunshot, and forces the third shot airborne as he grabs the assassin's arms. It is Kenny, who is convinced somehow that he has killed the right enemy. Whatever Kenny says is obliterated, as other men and police rush forward to help Pvt. Kelly,

swallowing up Kenny and his broken vision. Onstage, there are screams and stunned silence, all of it confused and with no form. Barnett makes his way to her crumpled form pathetically, as Haven, who has lost his toupee in the melee, takes charge with extraordinary gentleness.

HAVEN
All right now, you get her. Get her here, Bud, help her up now. Come on, I'm all right, here we go.

Bud, Tom, Barnett, Tommy Brown, members of the choir, and others pick her up with care and walk through the columns as if their mission had hope — somehow knowing better.

BARNETT (quietly)
Oh, man, I can't stop that blood, man.

Haven is onstage, oblivious to his blood-soaked arm. He talks into the microphone to try to cut through the chaos in the audience.

HAVEN
Y'all take it easy now.

Police security has suddenly increased and Hal Phillip Walker and the black limousine cavalcade exit at high speed behind a police car whose siren screams into the continuing chaos.

HAVEN
This isn't Dallas, this is Nashville . . . You show 'em what we're made of. They can't do this to us here in Nashville.

The crowd responds a little but not much. Delbert comes up behind him.

HAVEN
Okay, everybody sing! Come on now, sing . . . (aside) I wish they had —

DEL
I think you . . . Let, let me help you.

HAVEN (looking around)
No I'm fine . . . I'm — you sing. You stay here and sing.

DEL
Haven, I think you've been hurt.

Haven turns around and thrusts the microphone into the near-by hand of Albequerque.

HAVEN
Sing!

DEL

Haven—

HAVEN

I'm all right...

And Delbert leads him off the stage.

DELBERT

Is there anyone down here can help us?

Albequerque begins to sing tentatively, still caught up in the event that's just taken place.

Somehow, in the scramble, Green runs into L.A. Joan who is crying, and he grabs her arm roughly and leads her out of the crowd. Bill rushes onto the stage to Mary and they leave immediately. Opal wanders through the crowd asking if anyone can tell her what happened—she was in the truck talking when the shots were fired. Triplette stands looking out somewhere, guilty, hollow, finished before he has begun.

Albequerque has found her voice and talks to the audience.

ALBEQUERQUE (singing)
They say this train
don't give out rides,
But it don't worry
me.

(The choir trickles forward
and joins her.)
All the world is takin'
sides
But it don't worry
me.
Cause in my empire
life is sweet,
Just ask any bum
you meet.
The fact may be, the
world ain't free,
But it don't worry
me.

ALBEQUERQUE

Come on, everybody, sing. Come on! (singing) It
don't worry me. It don't worry me...

They start slowly with her voice soaring out, giving them strength. Finally they respond and their panic turns around on itself. Linnea stands devastated, somehow unable to reconcile any of it with the song. Triplette starts offstage

past Albequerque who scoops up the white carnations and
throws them into the audience, past Sueleen Gay, who still
waits in the wings, and silently past Delbert, who pushes by
Sueleen to get to Linnea so he can take her home to the
children.

DELBERT
Come on honey. Come on.

Pvt. Kelly, who has been numbly standing next to the platform, turns and walks out through the crowd. He has to catch a
bus back to Fort Campbell — his five-day pass is up at six.

ALBEQUERQUE AND
AUDIENCE AND CHOIR
You may say that I
ain't free,
But it don't worry
me.
The price of bread
may worry some,
But it don't worry
me.
Tax relief may never
come,
But it don't worry
me.
Economy's
depressed, not me.
My spirit's high as it
can be.
You may say that I
ain't free,
But it don't worry me
Oh, it don't worry
me.
It don't worry me.
You may say that I
ain't free,
But it don't worry
me...
Oh, it don't worry
me,

Albequerque and the audience continue to sing. For a moment, we see the faces of mothers and fathers and children
and babies. Then we pull back and see the whole event as
the camera pans up to the sky signifying...

THE END

NEW ROOTS FOR THE NATION

Fellow taxpayers and stockholders in America.

On the first Tuesday in November we have to make some vital decisions about our management. Let me go directly to the point: I'm for doing some replacing. I've discussed the Replacement Party with people all over this country, and I'm often confronted with the statement, "I don't want to get mixed up in politics," or "I'm tired of politics," or "I'm not interested." Almost as often, someone says, "I can't do anything about it anyway."

Let me point out two things. Number one: All of us are deeply involved with politics whether we know it or not, and whether we like it or not. And... number two... we can do something about it. When you pay forty-eight cents for a loaf of bread instead of twenty-six, that's politics. When you pay sixty-five cents per gallon for gas, instead of thirty-one cents, that's politics. When you pay more for an automobile than it cost Columbus to make his first voyage to America, that's politics.

There is no question about being involved; the question is, "What to do?" It is the very nature of government to strain at a gnat and swallow a camel. As loyal citizens, we accept our take-home pay, understand most of the deductions and even to a degree, come to expect them. However, when a government begins to force its citizens to swallow the camel, it's time to pause and do some accounting. If the Chairman of the Board or the President of your company had been running your business the way Washington has been running our business, you'd be asking a lot of questions. And you would find out what you already know: We have some problems that money alone won't solve.

Now, I know something about money; anybody who grew up without it, knows a lot about money. I know more about money than some of the rich because I never had any until I was twenty-seven. I know something of what money can do, and more important, I know something of what it can't do. In time I did become President of the Corporation . . . Chairman of the Board . . . but my first job was back on my grandfather's farm.

We would come home from the fields at night and my grandfather, who was busy at the store most of the day, always asked for a report. He never asked how many acres we had planted, how many pounds we had picked, how many rows we had hoed . . . he always asked, "Did you get done today what you should have done?" That was all he ever asked. And he didn't want a speech. He didn't want a dissertation. He was not interested in elocution. He wanted a one syllable answer to a reasonable question: "Did you get done today what you should have done?"

Sometimes we gave excuses. The cultivator broke... we ran out of seed corn... it was a hundred-and-two in the shade. And my grandfather would say, "I didn't ask you about the cultivator or the seed corn or the weather; I asked if you got done today what you should have done. Yes... or no?"

Apply that simple and direct question to Washington, to any agency or bureau, to either House of Congress, to the ones who ought to know; ask whether they have got done what they should have done. Instead of a one syllable answer, you'll get one of two things: either a long-winded devious excuse, or a complicated lawyeristic remedy of what's going to be next month, next year, or next generation. What this country needs is some one syllable answers. We need to replace the wornout, burdensome, red-tape bureaucracy that won't let our farmers produce when half the world is hungry... won't let our builders build when legions are ill-housed... won't let our teachers teach when generations thirst for knowledge; we need to replace it with some one syllable efforts toward common sense.

This country is crying out not for a genius, not for an orator, not for a scholar, but simply for a good man with at least half a notion toward common sense. A good man with some one syllable answers could do a lot for this country.

A newspaper... and incidentally, I applaud the press and the healthy role it plays in this country... a newspaper — I don't recall which one — printed a story the other day saying I ought not to be running for President because I'm not a lawyer. Well, I'm not a lawyer; that part is correct. In that same article there was considerable lambasting of Congress and the courts. As I read the article... which was rather good, I thought... I wanted to be able to ask the writer face-to-face, "Who do you think is running Congress? Farmers, engineers, teachers, businessmen?" No, my friends. Congress is run by lawyers; lock, stock, and barrel... breadtray to horsetrough. You wonder what's wrong? A lawyer is trained for two things and two things only: to clarify... that's one... and to confuse, that's the other thing. He does whichever is to his client's advantage.

You ever ask a lawyer the time of day? He told you how to make a watch, didn't he? Ever ask a lawyer how to get to Mr. Jones' house in the country? You got lost, didn't you? Ever know anybody to win a big damage suit? But the lawyer ended up with all the money, didn't he?

Congress is composed of five-hundred-and-thirty-five individuals. Two-hundred-and-eighty-eight are lawyers. And you wonder what's wrong in Congress. The Senate alone...the world's most select and exclusive body... is composed of one-hundred people. Sixty-seven are lawyers. Sixty-seven percent.

There are more than eighty-million laborers in this country, more than two-million teachers, three-million farmers, nine-million small businessmen... only three-hundred-and-seventy-five-thousand lawyers. Not two-tenths of one percent of the population of this country and they make our laws, administer our laws, interpret our laws... no wonder we often know how to make a watch but we don't know the time of day.

No wonder it takes six or seven years to get a final decision... if you get one at all... when somebody happens to rob your store, or break into your house, or murder your neighbor.

Businessmen know how to run big companies, teachers know how to run enormous schools, farmers know how to run vast farms, engineers know how to run gigantic projects. Yes, I'm talking about replacement. Replacing this lawyeristic red-taped and blank-taped government with the "yes" and "no" language of farmers and teachers and engineers and businessmen. I'm not pessimistic about this country; I'm an optimist. But I don't go around looking for eggs in a cuckoo clock. Time for replacements... new roots for this nation... the time is long past due.

My grandfather had an expression, "All talk and no do." And I remember a story about his younger days when he had taken a farm with buildings so run-down a rat was afraid to spend the night in the barn. And the land so poor it wouldn't sprout whip-poorwill peas. And mostly with his own bare hands he made that farm into a near-showplace. Then one day the preacher came by to admire all the improvements, and he said, "Isn't it wonderful what God and man working together can do?" And my grandfather smiled and said, "That's right, Reverend, but you should have seen this place when the Lord was working it by himself!"

With all due reverence, I'm merely suggesting the Lord is not going to take on any janitorial services for our houses of government. If there's any cleaning up done, we're going to have to do it. If the books are to be balanced, we're going to have to balance them. The Lord is not going to do the replacing, and the "powers that be" are certainly not going to replace themselves. That old truth remains: "There is no such thing as a free lunch."

Some very funny notions have developed in American politics. Somewhere we got exposed and fell victim to the idea that all good laws would last forever. And all bad laws would pass away like a disagreeable dream. Take the matter of treating every employee alike.

The United States government says it wants you, as an employer, to treat everybody with fairness. That's a wonderful thing; I wholly approve. But let's see what the United States government itself does. If you are an ordinary government employee, you must retire no later than age seventy. However, if you are a federal judge, you may remain in office for life. I say this is a gross injustice. Why not equal treatment for all? If the janitor and the clerk must retire at seventy, why not the judge? In truth as in so many cases, Washington is preaching a doctrine of fairness, but practicing a doctrine of rank discrimination.

Take a look at the seniority system in Congress. It's a very simple proposition: if the average business or company operated under the seniority system the janitor, or the mailboy, or the junior clerk, would always wind up Chairman of the Board. It simply doesn't make sense. I know of no other place in the world where seniority is so cherished, and where intelligence and ability are so disregarded.

Look at the electoral college. Congress and the courts have gone to great lengths to emphasize the one-man one-vote rule. The electoral college is a flagrant violation of that rule. There is a principle in nature which no art can overturn: that the more simple anything is, the less liable it is to be disordered, and the easier repaired when broken.

Let's apply this maxim to the electoral college, abolish it, and thereby eliminate at least one lawyeristic complication of government. We have become so complicated there is no breathing space.

Let's consider our National Anthem. Nobody knows the words! Nobody can sing it! Nobody understands it! It doesn't arouse half as much patriotic emotion as "My Country 'Tis of Thee" or "America," but Congress in its infinite wisdom gave us "The Star Spangled Banner" in 1931. I suppose all the lawyers supported it because a lawyer wrote the words and a judge wrote the tune.

Read it through carefully... and I say read it because I know you can't sing it... read all four verses and you'll understand what I'm talking about. Yessir, I would support work and vote for replacement. Change our National Anthem back to something people could understand, back to something that would make a light shine in their faces, back to something they could sing with their hearts, instead of humming and mumbling through a confused series of frowns. People can understand Woody Guthrie.

People can sing "This Land is Your Land" and what's more, they can feel it.

Oh, I know the political physicians are laughing but not quite as loud today as they were yesterday. Not quite as loud as they were before the Wisconsin primaries, or Maryland, or Florida. Tomorrow... next week... they may be laughing less and less, and who knows about November? Only the people should know. The people are always ahead. And when they cease to be ahead, democracy as we know it will cease to be.

Security should be the first and last design of all government. Security of mind, of heart, of health, security abroad, security at home. The business of law and order touches every citizen, but we must do more than maintain law and order; we must get to the roots of lawlessness and disorder.

Now, I'm well aware that security is not found on an isolated island anymore than it's found in the great urban areas of this country where a keeper of the peace is required for every two-hundred-and-fifty people. Let us go to the heart of the matter; fathom the causes of unrest and trouble. Be it drugs, poverty, affluence, carelessness, apathy, whatever, and set our goal as one of correction and prevention instead of all-out punishment. With proper leadership and effort we can wipe out crime as surely as this country wiped out polio or smallpox. I can think of no sensible reason why New York must of necessity have twelve-thousand major crimes committed for every one-thousand committed in Tokyo, yet these are the true figures.

The sick and afflicted must be better cared for in this country. By and large, our patchwork quilt has proved to be a blanket of false security. Today in America, with its unmatched resources, it is exceedingly ridiculous, a total absurdity, that any citizen with any ailment, mental or physical, should go medically unattended. Every community needs special programs for the mentally ill, the aged, the retarded, the handicapped. To fall short in these areas is to bring disgrace on all our houses, and so far we have fallen woefully short.

What we need first and foremost is a common sense approach, nothing complicated, nothing lawyeristic. Can it possibly make sense to regiment farms and farmers when people are ill-fed if not downright hungry? To tax the salaries of people on poverty-level incomes then turn around and give back in food-stamps twice the amount of the tax? Not to mention the cost of collection or distribution.

Does it make sense to let the petroleum giants increase their prices at will, adding to an already staggering profit, but tell the little filling station owner in his khakis he can't charge one penny more? Does it make sense that the churches should remain untaxed on their vast holdings of land and corporate investments? Does it make sense that a multi-million-dollar income should go untaxed year after year?

I believe it is time to begin... time for replacement... time to establish new roots for this nation. The beginning is always the most important step of any journey, and the period of waiting the most dangerous time, for on the vast plains of hesitation lie the bleaching bones of those who sat down to wait, and waiting, died.

Let us begin.

Stamp your thundering approval on the Replacement Party and tell whoever will listen, "We will not swallow the camel!"

No... all will not be easy but we will bask in the satisfaction of having done what we should have done... and if we don't get it done today... we may run out of tomorrows!

by THOMAS HAL PHILLIPS

LYRICS

200 YEARS

(Richard Baskin and Henry Gibson)

My mother's people came by ship and fought at Bunker Hill.
My daddy lost a leg in France, I have his medals still.
My brother served with Patton, I saw action in Algiers.
Oh we must be doin' something right to last two hundred years.

I pray my sons won't go to war, but if they must they must.
I share our country's motto and in God I place my trust.
We may have had our ups and downs, our times of trials and tears.
But we must be doing something right to last two hundred years.

I've lived through two depressions, and seven dust bowl droughts.
Floods, locusts and tornadoes, but I don't have any doubts.
We're all a part of history, why Old Glory waves to show
How far we've come along till now, how far we've got to go.

It's been hard work but every time we get into a fix,
Let's think of what our children face in two ought seven six.
It's up to us to pave the way with our blood and sweat and
    tears.
For we must be doing something right to last two hundred
    years.

Lion's Gate Music Co.,
Landscape Music Co.,
Silvery Moon Music and
Plumbago Publishing Co.

BLUEBIRD

(Ronee Blakley)

I've been goin' down that long lonesome road boy,
I been doin' it for a while.
I've been goin' down that long lonesome road babe,
Lookin' for a special smile.
I worked the bars, New York to Frisco,
But I could never make it pay.
You know how money goes, it slips right through your fingers,
One more dollar one more day.

The bluebird he has no money
The bluebird he has no kin'
The bluebird, he wears no time clock
He answers to the wind.

I've been goin' down that same old road babe,
But like the world I'm addin' on some years.
I've shoved a hundred million quarters in that jukebox,
I've served a barrel full of beer.
I've listened to some troubles in my life time,
I've seen a lot of grown men cry.
You know that old tune, "Over The Rainbow,"
If the bluebird flies there why can't I?

I've always lived my life like there ain't no tomorrow
Guess I always have and I always will.
Behind me all my yesterdays go stretchin' out like box cars,
Disappearin' 'round some hill.
I always thought that life was for livin'

But nothin' is as easy as it seems.
I wish I was a bluebird flyin,
Instead of always tryin' just to find the rainbow in my dreams.

Lion's Gate Music Co. and
Sawtooth Music

MEMPHIS

(Karen Black)

Well I'd like to go to Memphis
but I don't know the way
and I'd like to tell you how I feel
but I don't know what to say
and I'd like to go to heaven
but I forgot how to pray
so just help me keep from sliding down some more.

When I tried to get back to him
I got lost on the way
I'd like to start again tomorrow
but I don't know what day it is
and I'd sure like to love you
if you'd show me the way
and just help me keep from sliding down some more,

well I don't know what it's like out there
but in here its getting darker
I've got a lot of things to share
but it sure is getting late.

well I'd like to give you all I've got
but I don't know what that is
and I'd like to take you with me
but I don't know where that is
and I know there must be something someplace
and some way to live
someone help me keep from sliding down some more,
some more.

Lion's Gate Music Co. and
Matter Music

ROLLING STONE

(Karen Black)

You walked me, sweet Joshua, down the country lane
You brought me, sweet Joshua, where the roses grow so tall.
You lay me down, Joshua, and you promised me your name.
And after that, that was all. That was all.

Rolling stone, rolling stone, gathers no moss
Old as the stars up above.
Rolling stone, rolling stone, gathers no moss.
But neither does it gather any love.

I saw you Joshua by the garden wall,
You brought her, sweet Joshua, where the roses lie in vain,
You broke her heart, Joshua, like so many ones before.
But someday you will understand the pain.

Chorus

Come round me, Joshua, and I will not see your face.
Walk with me Joshua and I'll say that I am lame.
I'll have, sweet Joshua, the child that you have made.
But I'll never let him mention your name.

Lion's Gate Music Co. and
Matter Music

DUES*

(Ronee Blakley)

It's that careless disrespect
I can't take no more baby.
And it's the way that you don't love me
When you say you do, baby.

It hurts so bad, it gets me down, down, down.
I want to walk away from the battle ground.
This hurtin' match, it ain't no good.
I'd give a lot to love you the way I used to do,
Wish I could.

You've got your own private world
I wouldn't have it no other way.
But lately, you've been hidin' your blues,
Pretendin' what you say.

Chorus

Writin' it down kinda makes me feel better,
Keeps me away from the blues.
I want to be nice to you, treat you right,
But how long can I pay these dues?

It hurts so bad, it gets me down, down, down.
I want to walk away from the battleground
This hurtin' match, it ain't no good.
I'd give a lot to love you the way I used to do,
Wish I could.
Wish I could.

Lion's Gate Music Co. and
Sawtooth Music

TAPEDECK IN HIS TRACTOR*

(Ronee Blakley)

He's got a tapedeck in his tractor and he listens to the local
     news
He finds out where the bass are biting while he's plowing to
     the country blues
He was a cowboy and he knew I loved him well
A cowboy's secrets you never tell
No, there's nothin' like the lovin' of a hard workin' cowboy
     man.

He's got a tapedeck in his tractor and he's plowin' up his
     daddy's land
He's got more horse sense than I've seen in any man
He was a cowboy and he knew I loved him well
A cowboy's secrets you never tell
No, there's nothin' like the lovin' of a hard workin' cowboy
     man.

On Saturday nights we go dancin' in town
And all the boys'll order up another round
When the summer comes, we look forward to the rodeo

On Saturday night we go to town
And all the boys will order up another round
When he rides saddle bronc, I wait to hear that whistle blow.

He's got a tapedeck in his tractor, I can hear him when he's
    comin' home.
Then he holds me in the rocking chair and sings me a love
    song
He was a cowboy and he knew I loved him well
A cowboy's secrets you never tell
No, there's nothin' like the lovin' of a hard workin' cowboy
    man.

Lion's Gate Music Co. and
Sawtooth Music

ONE, I LOVE YOU

(Richard Baskin)

When I feel my life perishing, I call you on the phone
You always fix me up when I get broken.
'Cause every time that I got hurt and went out of control
You knew the fears I felt before I spoke them.
You'd sing me...

One, I love you
Two, I'm thinkin' of you
Three, I'll never let you go.
Four, I miss you
Five, I want to kiss you
Six, I won't leave you no more.

I feel my time here vanishing like waves upon the sand
With nothing to replace it but invention.
So I make my rhymes and I sing my tunes,
Still they don't understand:
To make 'em laugh was never my intention.

One, I love you
Two, I'm thinkin' of you
Three, I'll never let you go
Four, I miss you,
Five, I want to kiss you
Six, I won't leave you no more.

Lion's Gate Music Co. and
Silvery Moon Music

KEEP A-GOIN'

(Richard Baskin & Henry Gibson)

If you strike a thorn on a rose,
    Keep a-goin'!
If it hails or if it snows,
    Keep a-goin'!
Ain't no use to sit an' whine,
When the fish ain't on your line;
Bait your hook an' keep a-tryin'
    Keep a-goin'!

When the weather kills your crop,
    Keep a-goin'!
It takes work to reach the top,
    Keep a-goin'!
Spose' you're out o' ev'ry dime,
Gittin' broke ain't any crime;
It'll all work out in time —
    Keep a-goin'!

When you're up against the wall,
    Keep a-goin'!
Swallow hard and just stand tall,
    Keep a-goin'!
When the skies look dark and grey.
Tell the world you'll find your way,
And don't forget to pray.
    Keep a-goin'!

When the doctor says you're through,
    Keep a-goin'!
He's a human just like you,
    Keep a-goin'!
Ain't no law says you must die,
Wipe the tears from off your eye.
Give old life another try,
    Keep a-goin'!

Trust the Good Lord up on high,
    Keep a-goin'!

Lion's Gate Music Co.,
Landscape Music Co.,
Silvery Moon Music and
Plumbago Publishing Co.

I'M EASY

(Keith Carradine)

It's not my way to love you just when no one's lookin'
It's not my way to take your hand if I'm not sure
It's not my way to let you see what's goin' on inside of me
When it's love you won't be needing, you're not free
Please stop pullin' at my sleeve if you're just playin'
If you won't take the things you make me want to give
I never cared too much for games, and this one's drivin' me
     insane
You're not half as free to wander as you claim.

But I'm easy, I'm easy
Give the word, I'll play your game as though that's how it
     ought to be
Because I'm easy.

Don't lead me on if there's nowhere for you to take me
If lovin' you would have to be a sometime thing
I can't put bars on my inside
My love is something I can't hide
It still hurts when I recall the times I tried.

But I'm easy, I'm easy
Take my hand and pull me down, I won't put up any fight
Because I'm easy.

Don't do me any favors, let me watch you from a distance
'Cause when you're near I find it hard to keep my head
And when your eyes throw light at mine
It's enough to change my mind,
Make me leave my cautious words and ways behind.

That's why I'm easy, I'm easy
Say you want me, I'll come running
Without taking time to think
Because I'm easy, I'm easy
Take my hand and pull me down, I won't put up any fight
Because I'm easy, I'm easy
Give the word, I'll play your game as though that's how it
     ought to be
Because I'm easy.

Lion's Gate Music Co. and
Easy Music

IT DON'T WORRY ME

(Keith Carradine)

The price of bread may worry some,
But it don't worry me
And tax relief may never come,
But it don't worry me
Economy's depressed, not me,
My spirit's high as it can be
And you might say that I ain't free
But it don't worry me.

It don't worry me
It don't worry me
You may say that I ain't free
But it don't worry me.

They say this train don't give out rides,
Well, it don't worry me
And all the world is takin' sides,
Well, it don't worry me
'Cause in my empire, life is sweet,
Just ask any 'bo you meet
And life may be a one way street,
But it don't worry me.

It don't worry me
It don't worry me
You may say that I ain't free
But it don't worry me.

Lion's Gate Music Co. and
Easy Music

MY IDAHO HOME*

(Ronee Blakley)

Mama and daddy raised me with lovin' care
They sacrificed, so I could have a better share
They fed me and nursed me and sent me to school
Mama taught me how to sing, daddy lived the golden rule.

When I think of the children, alone and afraid, abandoned
    and wild, like a fatherless child
I think of my mama and how she could sing harmony with my
    daddy, our laughter would ring...

Down the highways, on the beaches
Just as far as memory reaches
I still hear daddy singin' his old army songs
We'd laugh and count horses as we drove along
We were young then, we were together
We could bear floods and fire and bad weather
But now that I'm older, grown up on my own
I still love mama and daddy best, and
My Idaho home.

Mama grew up on the prairies of Kansas
She was tender and sweet
The dust and tornadoes blew 'round her
But they left her straight up on her feet.
My daddy grew up on his own, more or less
His mama died when he was just eleven
He had seven sisters to raise him
But he dreamed of his mama in heaven
His daddy drank whiskey and had a sharp eye
He sold chicken medicine farmers would buy
Together they hunted the fields and the farms
When his daddy died, my daddy rested in my momma's
    arms.

Lion's Gate Music Co. and
Sawtooth Music

Producer/Director **ROBERT ALTMAN**
Executive Producers **JERRY WEINTRAUB**
MARTIN STARGER
Associate Producers **BOB EGGENWEILER**
THOMAS HAL PHILLIPS
SCOTT BUSHNELL
Production Manager/Assistant Director **TOMMY THOMPSON**
Assistant Director **ALAN RUDOLPH**
DGA Trainee **VICTOR HSU**
Production Co-ordinator **KELLY MARSHALL**
Production Accountant **ANN TAIT**
Production Executive **JIM KOEHLER**
Production Secretary **ELAINE BRADISH**
Writer **JOAN TEWKESBURY**
Political Campaign **THOMAS HAL PHILLIPS**
Script Supervisor **JOYCE KING**
Director of Photography **PAUL LOHMANN**
Camera Operator **ED KOONS**
Camera Assistants **JIM BLANFORD**
HARRY WALSH III
MICHAEL WALSH
Stillman **JIM COE**
Sound **JIM WEBB**
CHRIS McLAUGHLIN
Sound System **LION'S GATE 8 TRACK SOUND**
Music Recorded by **GENE EICHELBERGER**
JOHNNY ROSEN
Electric Gaffer **RANDY GLASS**
MIKE MARLETT
Property Master **BOB ANDERSON**
Key Grips **HARRY REZ**
EDDIE LARA
Craft Service **LINN ZUCKERMAN**
Make-up **TOMMY THOMPSON**
Wardrobe **JULES MELILLO**
Hairdresser **ANN WADLINGTON**
Casting (Local) **JOANN DOSTER**
Press Liaison **SUE BARTON**

Production Assistants   JAC CASHIN
ANGEL DOMINGUEZ
MARK EGGENWIELER
ROGER FRAPPIER
RON HECHT
ALLAN HIGHFILL
MAYSIE HOY
Musical Director   RICHARD BASKIN
Film Editors   SID LEVIN A.C.E.
DENNIS HILL
Assistant Film Editors   TONY LOMBARDO
TOM WALLS
Apprentice Film Editor   STEVE ALTMAN
Title Design   DAN PERRI
Transportation Captain   JIM THORNSBERRY
Transportation Co-captain   GENE CLINESMITH
Drivers   JOHN BRUMBY
RICK MERCIER
CHUCK HAUER
Caterer   MICKEY CHONOS
Book Cover Illustration   WILLIAM MYERS JR.
Acknowledgments to   TONY PEYSER and DEBBIE ROSS
who helped prepare this book